THE Authoritative CALVIN AND HOBBES

Other Books by Bill Watterson

Calvin and Hobbes
Something Under the Bed Is Drooling
Yukon Ho!
Weirdos From Another Planet!
The Revenge of the Baby-Sat
Scientific Progress Goes "Boink"
Attack of the Deranged Mutant Killer Monster Snow Goons
Homicidal Psycho Jungle Cat
The Days Are Just Packed
It's a Magical World
The Calvin and Hobbes Tenth Anniversary Book
There's Treasure Everywhere

Treasury Collections

The Essential Calvin and Hobbes
The Calvin and Hobbes Lazy Sunday Book
The Indispensable Calvin and Hobbes

THE *Authoritative* CALVIN AND HOBBES

A Calvin and Hobbes Treasury

by BILL WATTERSON

Includes Cartoons From
Yukon Ho! and *Weirdos From Another Planet!*

SCHOLASTIC INC.
New York Toronto London Auckland Sydney

Calvin and Hobbes is syndicated internationally by Universal Press Syndicate.

ISBN 0-590-81923-2

12 11 10 9 8 7 6 2 3/0

Printed in the U.S.A. 14
First Scholastic printing, September 1998

To Doctor Dave and
Fellow Moosers John, Brad, and The Frey

Calvin and HOBBES
by WATTERSON
ARRGH! I'M NEVER GOING TO BE ABLE TO MEMORIZE ALL THESE DUMB VOCABULARY WORDS!
TRANSMOG-RIFIER
ZAP
TRANSMOG-RIFIER
WUMP WUMP
WUM
HOW CAN ONE LITTLE KID MAKE SO MUCH NOISE?
CALVIN, WHAT ARE YOU DOING UP THERE?! YOU SOUND LIKE AN ELEPHANT! YOU'RE SUPPOSED TO BE DOING YOUR HOMEWORK!

I AM DOING MY HOMEWORK!

HA! WHAT A GREAT IDEA! ELEPHANTS NEVER FORGET, SO MEMORIZING THIS WAS A SNAP! I'M ALL DONE!
NOW I CAN GO OUT AND PLAY!
HEY HOBBES, GUESS WHAT'S DIFFERENT ABOUT ME!
Z
AUGH!!

CALVIN! MY, HOW YOU'VE GROWN SINCE I LAST SAW YOU!
I TRANSMOGRIFIED MYSELF TO FINISH MY HOMEWORK FASTER.
C'MON, LET'S FIND A MUD HOLE TO PLAY IN! ELEPHANTS LOVE MUD!
GREAT! YOU CAN TELL ME SOME ELEPHANT JOKES THERE!
HI CALVIN. BOY, LOOK AT *YOU*!
IMPRESSIVE, EH? HOW DID YOU EVEN RECOGNIZE ME?
I'LL ADMIT IT WASN'T EASY.
HEY, HERE'S A RIDDLE HOBBES MADE UP. WHO DO HOBBES AND I LOOK LIKE? CAN YOU GUESS?
I GIVE UP.
THE REPUBLICAN PARTY AND TAMMANY HALL! SEE? PRETTY GOOD, HUH? HA HA HA HA!
FORGET IT, HOBBES. POLITICAL HUMOR IS JUST TOO SOPHISTICATED FOR GIRLS.
HMPH. HER LOSS!

CALVIN, TIME FOR DINNER!
UH OH. MOM WILL HAVE A FIT IF I GO TO THE TABLE AS AN ELEPHANT.
YOU'D BETTER TRANSMOGRIFY BACK TO A KID.
THE TRANSMOGRIFIER IS STILL IN MY ROOM. WE'LL HAVE TO SNEAK UPSTAIRS! SHHHH!
CALVIN, DID I HEAR YOU COME... OH NO!
CALVIN, YOU... AUGHH! WHAT HAVE YOU BEEN DOING?!
IT'S OK, MOM! THIS ISN'T PERMANENT! I WAS JUST GOING TO TRANSMOGRIFY MYSELF BACK TO THE WAY I USED TO BE!
I'LL SAY YOU WILL! WHAT A MESS! GET INTO THE TUB THIS INSTANT!

THERE. I HOPE *THIS* MAKES MOM HAPPY! HAND ME A FEW MORE TOWELS, AND THEN I'LL GO TRANSMOGRIFY.
OK, THE DIAL IS SET FOR "CALVIN." READY?
READY!
ZAP
TRANSMOG RIFIER
AHH! BACK TO NORMAL! I'D BETTER GET DOWN TO THE DINNER TABLE.. ..ALTHOUGH I'M GOING TO WISH I'D STAYED THE WAY I WAS, IF MOM FIXED SOME VEGGIE GLOP.
BRING ME UP WHATEVER YOU DON'T LIKE, OK?

SO LET'S HEAR ONE OF THE VOCABULARY WORDS YOU LEARNED.
OK. UM, LET'S SEE... ONE WAS.. UH, HMM... WELL, UH...
I THINK YOU'D BETTER SPEND A LITTLE MORE TIME WITH YOUR BOOK AFTER DINNER, HMM?
NO, NO, I REMEMBER THEM WHEN I'M AN ELEPHANT! I JUST DON'T KNOW THEM NOW! DON'T WORRY, I'LL TRANSMOGRIFY MYSELF BEFORE SCHOOL TOMORROW, AND I'LL DO FINE! REALLY!
YOU KNOW HOBBES, IF IT WASN'T FOR YOU, I'D NEVER HAVE ANY FUN AT ALL.
DON'T MENTION IT. I'M LEARNING SOME GOOD WORDS THIS WAY! MMM, YOU KNOW, THESE BEETS AREN'T BAD. ..AND THEY'RE CERTAINLY "SALUBRIOUS."
CAPT. NAPALM
WATTERSON
The End.

Calvin and HOBBES
by WATTERSON
WHEW! THIS MUST BE THE BIGGEST HILL IN THE STATE!
KIND OF FRUSTRATING, ISN'T IT? I WISH DAD WOULD GET TRANSFERRED TO THE ANDES.
LET'S GO DOWN THE HILL AND SEE IF WE CAN TRAVEL INTO THE FUTURE.
GO INTO THE FUTURE? HOW?
IT'S EASY! ALL WE HAVE TO DO IS GET GOING REAL FAST AND WE'LL TIME-WARP!
HA HA! FASTER! FASTER!
GOSH, WHAT DO YOU SUPPOSE THE FUTURE WILL BE LIKE?
WHO KNOWS? FLYING CARS AND CITIES BUILT ON CLOUDS, MAYBE!
JUST THINK OF ALL THE WEIRD THINGS WE CAN TELL PEOPLE WE SAW! OH BOY!
HEY, WE'RE AT THE BOTTOM OF THE HILL. I DIDN'T FEEL ANY TIME WARP, DID YOU?
NOPE.
BUT LOOK! IT'S TWO MINUTES LATER THAN WHEN WE STARTED! WE'RE IN THE FUTURE!!
HMM...THINGS HAVEN'T IMPROVED. I'M DISAPPOINTED.
WATTERSON

GOODNESS, YOU'RE FILTHY. INTO THE TUB WITH YOU.
I OBEY THE LETTER OF THE LAW, IF NOT THE SPIRIT.
LET'S HEAR SOME WATER RUNNING!
NUTS.

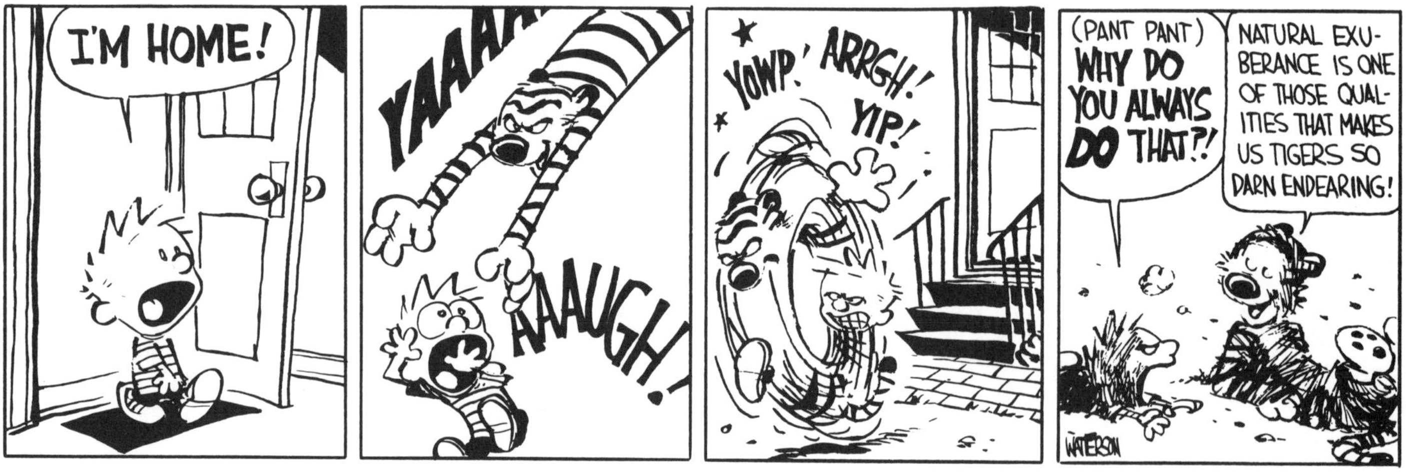
I'M HOME!
AAAUGH!
YOWP!
ARRGH!
YIP!
(PANT PANT) WHY DO YOU ALWAYS DO THAT?!
NATURAL EXUBERANCE IS ONE OF THOSE QUALITIES THAT MAKES US TIGERS SO DARN ENDEARING!

I'M HOME!
YAAA... HUH?? UH OH!
HA HA! FOOLED YOU!!
ELAPSED TURNAROUND TIME, POINT EIGHT SECONDS.
HA! STUPID TIGER.

I'M HOME!
... HELLO?
HOBBES ??
SIX... FIVE ... FOUR..
WATTERSON

I'M HOME.
I'M HOME.
I'M HOME!
..WELL-L-L ?!
SO YOU'RE HOME.
WATTERSON

CALVIN STEPS UP TO THE PLATE, AND THE OUTFIELD HEADS FOR THE BLEACHERS. IT'S SURE TO BE ANOTHER "HOMER," FOLKS.
HERE'S THE PITCH!
BONK!
NOT SURPRISINGLY, THE PITCHER DECIDES TO "WALK" CALVIN.
WATTERSON

Calvin and HobbEs
by WATTERSON
"BEFORE BEGINNING ANY HOME-PLUMBING REPAIR, MAKE SURE YOU POSSESS THE PROPER TOOLS FOR THE JOB."
"CHECK THE FOLLOWING LIST OF HANDY EXPLETIVES, AND SEE THAT YOU KNOW HOW TO USE THEM."
CALVIN WAKES UP ONE MORNING TO FIND HE NO LONGER EXISTS IN THE THIRD DIMENSION! HE IS 2-D!
THINNER THAN A SHEET OF PAPER, CALVIN HAS NO SURFACE AREA ON THE BOTTOM OF HIS FEET! HE IS IMMOBILE!
ONLY BY "WAVING" HIS BODY CAN CALVIN CREATE ENOUGH FRICTION WITH THE GROUND TO MOVE!
HAVING WIDTH BUT NO THICKNESS, CALVIN IS VULNERABLE TO THE SLIGHTEST GUST OF WIND!
TO AVOID DRAFTS, HE TWISTS HIMSELF INTO A TUBE, AND ROLLS ACROSS THE FLOOR!
WATTERSON
SOMEONE IS COMING! CALVIN QUICKLY STANDS UP STRAIGHT.
TURNING PERFECTLY SIDEWAYS, HE IS A NEARLY INVISIBLE VERTICAL LINE! NO ONE WILL NOTICE!
HEY DAD, KNOW WHY YOU DIDN'T SEE ME ALL MORNING?? I WAS TWO-DIMENSIONAL!
HMMM, I'LL BET YOU CAN'T DO IT ALL AFTERNOON, TOO...
DEAR!

I COULDN'T READ IT BECAUSE MY PARENTS FORGOT TO PAY THE GRAVITY BILL.

MAKE A PREDICTION, HOBBES.
WHAT FOR?
SO WE CAN SEE IF YOU HAVE ESP.
OK, I PREDICT YOU'LL FIND AN IRRESISTIBLE ATTRACTION TO A MUD HOLE.
!
HA HA. YOU STAY AWAY FROM ME.
IT'S GOING TO COME TRUE! I CAN FEEL IT!

HEY DAD, HOW DOES A CARBURETOR WORK?
I CAN'T TELL YOU.
WHY NOT?
IT'S A SECRET.
NO IT ISN'T! YOU JUST DON'T KNOW!

THIS IS A JOB FOR...
AACKK!
WAAUGHHH!!
FOR...?
...SOMEONE ELSE.
WATERSON

TIME FOR BED, CALVIN.
IT'S A FREE COUNTRY. I CAN DO WHAT I WANT.
WATERSON
GOOD NIGHT.
COMMUNISTS!

OH NO, I HAVE TO GO TO THE BATHROOM! THE MONSTERS WILL GET ME AS SOON AS I SET FOOT ON THE FLOOR!
I KNOW! PUT YOUR PILLOW DOWN AS A DECOY. WHILE THEY'RE EATING THAT, YOU CAN SLIP OUT!
GREAT IDEA!
I'M COMING OUT OF BED NOW! HERE I AM, ALL FAT AND SQUISHY!
THEY TOOK IT! MAN, LOOK AT THE FEATHERS FLY! YOU'D BETTER HURRY!
NO, I'VE DECIDED TO STAY HERE AND WET THE BED. BUT IT'S OK WITH ME IF YOU DON'T WANT TO STAY.
WATERSON

Calvin and Hobbes
by WATTERSON
CROQUET IS A GENTLEMAN'S GAME.
THAT'S HARD TO BELIEVE.
I'VE PLAYED BEFORE AND I CAN TELL YOU THE TEMPTATION TO MISUSE THESE THINGS IS AWFUL.
HEY, DON'T PUT THE WICKETS SO FAR APART.
THIS IS THE WAY THEY'RE SUPPOSED TO BE.
NO IT ISN'T, YOU BIG CHEATER. YOU'RE JUST DOING THIS BECAUSE YOU CAN HIT THE BALL HARDER THAN I CAN.
CHEATER?? WHO TOOK THE LUCKY RED BALL WHEN I WASN'T LOOKING?
I GOT TO PICK FIRST BECAUSE YOU DID LAST TIME!
THAT'S A LIE! YOU ALWAYS TAKE THE LUCKY RED BALL FIRST!
CALL ME A LIAR, WILL YOU? WELL, YOU'RE JUST A POOP HEAD! SO THERE!
POTTY MOUTH! POTTY MOUTH! CALVIN IS A POTTY MOUTH!
THBPBPTHPT!
WATTERSON
YOU'RE ASKING FOR A TOOTHLESS MOUTH, BUSTER!
YEAH? SAYS YOU AND WHAT ARMY? YOU COULDN'T KNOCK THE TEETH OUT OF A MOSQUITO!
HA! MOSQUITOS DON'T EVEN HAVE TEETH! THAT SHOWS HOW DUMB YOU ARE!
COMPARED TO YOU, I'M EINSTEIN! LEGGO MY LEG!
OW! GO STICK YOUR NOSE IN A RUBBER HOSE, YOU WALKING FLEA CONDO!
I'D SAY IT TAKES ONE TO KNOW ONE, BOZO! WHY DON'T YOU GO PLAY IN THE FOOD PROCESSOR!
IT'S GETTING DARK, CALVIN. C'MON INSIDE!
AW MOM, WE'RE RIGHT IN THE MIDDLE OF A CROQUET GAME!

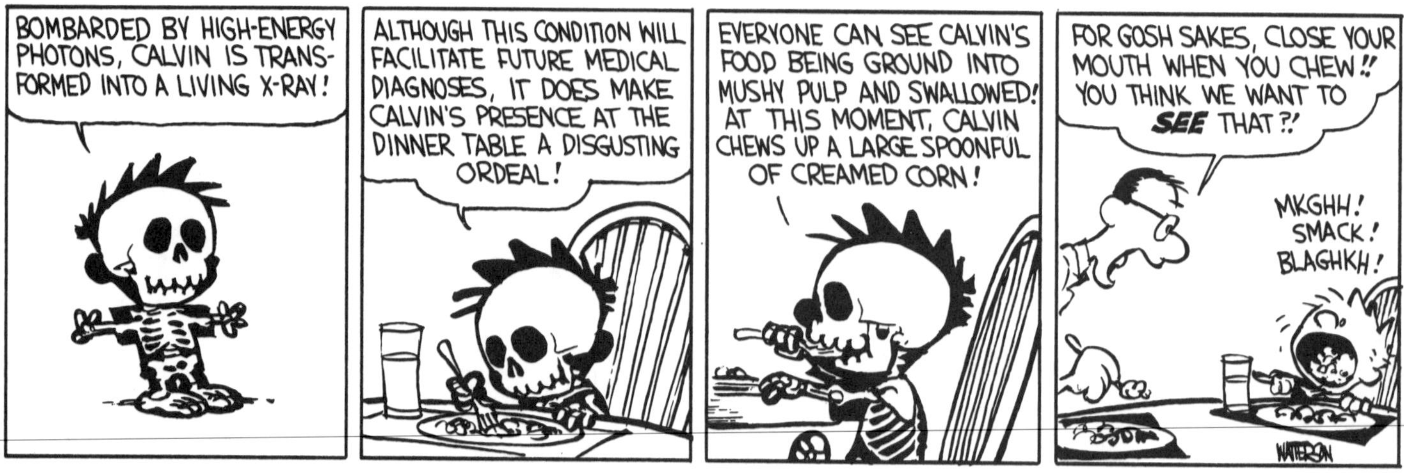
BOMBARDED BY HIGH-ENERGY PHOTONS, CALVIN IS TRANSFORMED INTO A LIVING X-RAY!
ALTHOUGH THIS CONDITION WILL FACILITATE FUTURE MEDICAL DIAGNOSES, IT DOES MAKE CALVIN'S PRESENCE AT THE DINNER TABLE A DISGUSTING ORDEAL!
EVERYONE CAN SEE CALVIN'S FOOD BEING GROUND INTO MUSHY PULP AND SWALLOWED! AT THIS MOMENT, CALVIN CHEWS UP A LARGE SPOONFUL OF CREAMED CORN!
FOR GOSH SAKES, CLOSE YOUR MOUTH WHEN YOU CHEW!! YOU THINK WE WANT TO ***SEE*** THAT?!
MKGHH! SMACK! BLAGHKH!
WATERSON

HERE'S A LITTLE TOWN.
HERE'S A STEAMSHOVEL SCOOPING OUT A GIANT HOLE.
HERE COMES THE BULLDOZER, PUSHING THOUSANDS OF BARRELS OF TOXIC NUCLEAR WASTE INTO THE GIANT HOLE.
OVER THE YEARS, THESE DANGEROUS POISONS SEEP INTO UNDERGROUND WATERWAYS.
THE CANCER RATE OF THE NEARBY LITTLE TOWN TRIPLES.
IF YOU WANT ME, I'LL BE UNDER THE BED.
WATERSON

A STRIKE?!? THAT PITCH WAS FOUR FEET ABOVE MY HEAD!
HA! IT WAS A ***PERFECT*** PITCH! YOU'RE JUST TOO SHORT!
YEAH? WELL, ***YOU'RE*** JUST TOO STUPID!
WELL, YOU'RE JUST TOO ***UGLY***!
KICK KICK KICK
KICK KICK KICK KICK
KICK KICK KICK
KICKING DUST IS THE ONLY PART OF THIS GAME WE REALLY LIKE.
WATERSON

WANT TO KNOW A FUNNY TRICK? WHEN SOMEBODY ISN'T LOOKING, YOU TIE HIS SHOES TOGETHER!
HA HA! THAT'S GREAT! LET'S GO FIND SOME SUCKER TO PULL IT ON!
YEAH!
WELL, WELL!
CLUNK!
WOO HOO HOO HOO HO
JUMP
JUMP

I'M HUNGRY. CAN I HAVE A SNACK?
SURE. HELP YOURSELF.
YOU CAN HAVE AN APPLE OR AN ORANGE FROM THE FRIDGE.
EVEN THOUGH WE'RE BOTH TALKING ENGLISH, WE'RE NOT SPEAKING THE SAME LANGUAGE.

BOY, I LOVE SUMMER VACATION.
I CAN FEEL MY BRAIN BEGINNING TO ATROPHY ALREADY.
SHHH..

Calvin and Hobbes
by
WATTERSON
I'M GOING OUTSIDE, MOM!
HOLD ALL MY CALLS.
CALVIN LOOKS AROUND. SOMETHING IS DIFFERENT.
THE ODD-COLORED TREE BEHIND HIM SLOWLY LIFTS UP! IT'S NOT A TREE AT ALL! IT'S A LEG!
OH NO! CALVIN IS THE SIZE OF A BUG TO A BUG! HE RUNS FOR HIS LIFE!
WATTERSON
A CLAW CRASHES WITH DEAFENING IMPACT! THE BUG IS TRYING TO STEP ON CALVIN! WHAT A HORRIBLE FATE!
CALVIN SCRAMBLES MADLY, PROMISING HIMSELF THAT HE'LL NEVER SQUISH ANOTHER BUG IF HE LIVES TO RETURN TO NORMAL SIZE!
SUDDENLY IN A SPRAY OF SLIME, THE BUG IS GONE! A MONSTROUS FROG LICKS ITS CHOPS! CALVIN IS SAVED!
AACCK! WHAT'S THAT ON MY PLATE?! GOOD HEAVENS, GET IT OFF THE TABLE!!
BUT MOM, FROGS ARE OUR FRIENDS!

LOOK HOBBES, I GOT A MAGIC CARPET!
WHAT'S SO MAGIC ABOUT IT?
MAGIC CARPETS FLY! YOU CAN RIDE THEM!
ISN'T THIS THE RUG FROM THE HALLWAY?
UP, RUG! UP! UP!
HEY, LOOK! IT WORKS! OK, RUG, WARP FACTOR FIVE!
IS THIS LEGAL? DO YOU HAVE YOUR REGISTRATION AND PROOF OF INSURANCE?
WATTERSON
WOW! I'VE NEVER BEEN ON A MAGIC CARPET BEFORE.
HMM...ME EITHER.
OK RUG, LET'S CRUISE AT 10,000 FEET!
WHEEEEEE
WATTERSON
GOSH, THIS SURE BEATS HAVING MOM DRIVE US AROUND! LET'S GO TO THE MALL AND HANG OUT!
DO WE GET COMPLI-MENTARY BAGS OF NUTS ON OUR FLIGHT?
HEY, LET'S FLY INTO THE CITY AND BUZZ DAD'S OFFICE!
HA! WON'T HE BE SURPRISED WHEN HE SEES US OUT HIS 20TH-FLOOR WINDOW!
WHAT IF HE'S MAD THAT WE TOOK THE HALLWAY RUG?
WATTERSON
WHAT'S TO GET MAD ABOUT? WE WIPED OUR FEET FIRST.
YEAH, BUT ALL THIS CITY MILEAGE MAY HURT THE RESALE VALUE.

OK, I THINK THAT'S DAD'S BUILDING UP AHEAD.
I'M NOT SURE WHERE HIS OFFICE IS, SO WE'LL JUST HAVE TO LOOK IN THE WINDOWS AS WE ZIP BY.
HEY! THERE HE IS! THERE'S DAD! HI, DAD! DAD, LOOK! OUT THE WINDOW!!
DARN IT! HE'S STILL READING THAT BRIEF. LOOK OUT THE WINDOW, DAD!
DID YOU BRING ANY ROCKS? I DIDN'T THINK TO.

HEY DAD! LOOK OUT THE WINDOW! ...I CAN'T BELIEVE HE'S JUST SITTING IN THERE.
WHY DOESN'T HE LOOK UP?
I GUESS HE'S PRETTY BUSY.
YEAH, BUT WE CAN'T SIT UP HERE ALL DAY! SHEESH. LET'S GO.
IF HE HAD NOTICED US, WE COULD'VE GIVEN HIM A RIDE HOME.
HMPH. I SAY LET HIM TAKE THE SMELLY OL' BUS IF HE CAN'T EVEN LOOK OUT THE WINDOW ONCE IN A WHILE. SERVES HIM RIGHT.

I'M HOME!
DAD! HOBBES AND I FLEW BY YOUR OFFICE WINDOW TODAY ON A RUG! WE SAW YOU WORKING.
WE WAVED AND HOLLERED, BUT YOU DIDN'T EVEN LOOK UP.
WE COULDN'T BELIEVE IT. YOU MISSED THE WHOLE THING!
I THOUGHT WE WERE CUTTING DOWN HIS SUGAR INTAKE.

Calvin and Hobbes
by WATTERSON
OY OH BOY OH BOY OH BOY OH BOY OH BOY OH BOY OH BOY OH BOY OH BOY
WAIT! WAIT! I'VE GOT TO SAVOR THIS MOMENT! THE BRILLIANCE OF IT ALL! I'M A GENIUS! A SHEER GENIUS!
SUSIE'S PLAYING ON THE SIDEWALK! NOW'S MY CHANCE TO USE THE SNOWBALL I'VE BEEN SAVING IN THE FREEZER!
SHE'LL NEVER EXPECT A SNOWBALL IN JUNE! BOY, WILL SHE BE MAD! HA HA HA!
THIS IS GOING TO BE GREAT! HERE IT COMES! OH BOY! OH BOY!
HEY SUSIE!!
PIFF
WATTERSON
I MISSED! DARN IT DARN IT DARN IT!! OF ALL THE MISERABLE LUCK!
AAARRGHH!
THERE MUST'VE BEEN A CROSS BREEZE! I CAN'T BELIEVE IT! I SAVED THAT SNOWBALL FOR THREE WHOLE MONTHS! I...
SCOOP SCOOP
I.. I... UH...
POW
THE IRONY OF THIS IS JUST SICKENING.

1988 ISN'T TOO FAR AWAY, DAD.
IF YOU'RE THINKING OF RUNNING FOR "DAD" AGAIN, YOU'D BETTER GET YOUR CAMPAIGN IN GEAR.
FRANKLY, THE POLLS LOOK GRIM. I DON'T THINK YOU'VE GOT MUCH OF A SHOT AT KEEPING THE OFFICE.
WATTERSON
I TAKE COMFORT IN THE FACT THAT NOT MANY PEOPLE WOULD WANT IT.
FLIPPANT REMARKS HAVE A WAY OF HAUNTING CANDIDATES, YOU KNOW.

THE CHAMELEON SITS MOTIONLESS.
AMAZINGLY, THE LIZARD CHANGES COLOR TO BLEND IN WITH HIS SURROUNDINGS.
MOMENTS LATER, HE IS VIRTUALLY INVISIBLE.
WATTERSON
I SEE YOU HIDING BACK THERE! NOW COME CLEAN UP THIS MESS YOU MADE IN THE KITCHEN!

HOLD STILL. THERE'S A MONSTER HORSEFLY ON YOUR HEAD.
POW!!
CAN YOU BELIEVE IT? I **MISSED**!
!
SO EXCUSE **ME** FOR TRYING TO HELP! YOU WANNA SCRATCH A STINGING WELT ALL DAY? **FINE**! GO AWAY!
NO, WAIT. THERE'S A MOSQUITO ON YOU.
WATTERSON

I WANNA HORSEY RIDE!
I'M BUSY, CALVIN.
YOU KNOW, DAD, IT WON'T BE LONG BEFORE I'M ALL GROWN UP. ONE DAY YOU'LL WAKE UP AND WONDER HOW ALL THE YEARS SLIPPED BY.
YOU'LL LOOK BACK AND SAY, "WHERE HAS THE TIME GONE? CALVIN'S SO BIG, IT'S HARD TO REMEMBER WHEN HE WAS SMALL ENOUGH THAT I COULD GIVE HIM HORSEY RIDES." ...BUT THOSE DAYS WILL BE LOST FOREVER.
I THINK I'VE WORKED THROUGH MY POTENTIAL GUILT NOW.
NO, NO! JUMP THE FENCE!
WATTERSON

I READ THAT GIRLS ARE MADE OF "SUGAR AND SPICE, AND EVERYTHING NICE"...
...WHEREAS BOYS ARE MADE OF "SNIPS AND SNAILS, AND PUPPY DOGS' TAILS."
HMPH.
SO WHAT ARE TIGERS MADE OF?
WATTERSON
"DRAGONFLIES AND KATYDIDS, BUT MOSTLY CHEWED-UP LITTLE KIDS."
OH, THAT'S CLEVER.

DO YOU HAVE ANY MONEY?
NOPE.
HMM... HOW CAN WE GET SOME?
WHO DO WE KNOW THAT WE COULD SUE?
WATTERSON

Calvin and HOBBES
by WATTERSON
WHAT'S WRONG WITH YOU, FISH? WHY WON'T YOU EAT THIS BIG, FAT, JUICY WORM?
...BESIDES THE OBVIOUS, I MEAN.
BOY, I HATE FISHING. THIS IS SO BORING!
LOOK, I CAN SEE A WHOLE BUNCH OF FISH DOWN THERE, BUT THEY'RE NOT BITING! LOUSY FISH!
BY GOLLY, I'M NOT GOING TO SIT HERE ALL DAY WAITING FOR THEM TO GET HUNGRY! HERE, HELP ME CARRY THIS ROCK.
WE'LL DUMP IT IN THE WATER AND BLAST THE FISH OUT. THEN WE CAN JUST PICK 'EM UP.
HEAVE!
KABLOOSH
OK, IT WAS A BAD IDEA! BUT I GOT WET TOO, RIGHT?
NO, NO, YOUR IDEA WAS FINE! WE JUST DIDN'T THROW IN A BIG ENOUGH OBJECT!
WATTERSON

...SO COULD I, MOM?
PLEASE?
..PLEEEAASE?
I STILL DON'T THINK GIVING HER "BAMBI EYES" IS GOING TO GET YOU A FLAME THROWER.
MAYBE I SHOULD SNIFFLE A LITTLE TOO, HUH?

WHAT A PERFECT DAY!
IF SOMETHING DOESN'T HAPPEN HERE SOON, I'M GONNA WACK OUT.

LOOK, A FIREFLY!
YOUR REAR HASN'T LIT, IF THAT'S WHAT YOU'RE WONDERING.
I CAN'T EVEN TELL WHAT MUSCLE TO FLEX.

HEY HOBBES, WANT TO SEE AN ANTELOPE?
AN ANTELOPE?!
C'MON!
SEE, SHE'S COMING DOWN THE LADDER TO HER BOYFRIEND'S CAR!
YOU'RE NOT LAUGHING.
IT'S NOT FUNNY.
WATTERSON

TOMORROW IS INDEPENDENCE DAY.
THE DECLARATION OF INDEPENDENCE SAYS EVERYONE IS CREATED EQUAL AND IS ENTITLED TO LIFE, LIBERTY AND THE PURSUIT OF HAPPINESS.
OH.
SO WHEN DOES PAUL REVERE RIDE THROUGH TOWN AND GIVE US OUR PRESENTS?
WATTERSON

BANG!
KAPWINNGG!
UP, UP AND AWAAAYY!
WATTERSON

Calvin and Hobbes
by WATTERSON
THE DREADED SCUM BEINGS FIRE! SPACEMAN SPIFF IS ***HIT!***
IT NEVER FAILS. I JUST WASHED AND WAXED THIS THING.
OUR HERO, THE INTREPID SPACEMAN SPIFF, STRUGGLES WITH THE CONTROLS OF HIS DAMAGED SPACECRAFT!
THE FREEM PROPULSION BLASTERS ARE USELESS! SPIFF CRASHES ONTO THE SURFACE OF AN ALIEN PLANET!
UNSCATHED, THE FEARLESS SPACE EXPLORER EMERGES FROM THE SMOLDERING WRECKAGE! HE IS MAROONED ON A HOSTILE WORLD!
SCORCHED BY TWIN SUNS, THE PLANET IS NOTHING BUT BARREN ROCK AND METHANE! THERE'S NO HOPE OF FINDING FOOD OR WATER!
SPIFF COLLAPSES! OH NO, A HIDEOUS ALIEN SPOTS HIM! IN HIS WEAKENED STATE, SPIFF IS NO MATCH FOR THE MONSTER! ***THIS COULD BE THE END!!***
WATTERSON
LUNCHTIME! I BROUGHT YOU A SANDWICH AND SOME LEMONADE.
BRING THE DISHES BACK WHEN YOU'RE DONE, OK?
...OH WELL.
THANKS, MOM.

Z
Z
Z
TAG!
THE GAME'S **OVER**, TUNA BRAIN.

SOMEBODY TOLD ME ROTTEN EGGS SMELL BAD.
THEY SMELL **TERRIBLE**.
PUT 'EM BACK, CALVIN.
WATTERSON

WATTERSON
I WANT 8 COOKIES TO GO, PLEASE.
THIS IS NOT A DRIVE-THRU! PUT THAT BACK IN THE GARAGE!

QUICK, MOM! ALIENS JUST LANDED IN THE BACK YARD! THEY DEMAND TO TALK TO YOU!
YOU GO ON OUT! I'LL GUARD THE COOKIES IN THE KITCHEN!
QUICK! HURRY!
SHE'S NOT BUYING THIS.
CALVIN, JUST HOW DUMB DO YOU THINK I AM?

WHAT DO YOU THINK IS THE SECRET TO HAPPINESS? IS IT MONEY, POWER OR FAME?
I'D CHOOSE MONEY. IF YOU HAVE ENOUGH MONEY, YOU CAN ***BUY*** POWER AND FAME. THAT WAY YOU'D HAVE IT ALL AND BE ***REALLY*** HAPPY!
HAPPINESS IS BEING FAMOUS FOR YOUR FINANCIAL ABILITY TO INDULGE IN EVERY KIND OF EXCESS.
I SUPPOSE THAT'S ***ONE*** WAY TO DEFINE IT.
THE PART I THINK I'D LIKE BEST IS CRUSHING PEOPLE WHO GET IN MY WAY.

LOOK! SOMEBODY POURED NEW CEMENT!
IS ANYONE LOOKING? WE COULD WRITE OUR INITIALS IN IT, OR MAKE A HAND PRINT, OR SOMETHING!
YEAH! "OR SOMETHING"!
I THINK WE'D BETTER FIND A HOSE QUICK!
I DIDN'T THINK IT WOULD SET UP SO FAST.

Calvin and Hobbes
by WATTERSON
Z Z Z Z Z Z
PSST... HEY, KID. C'MERE UNDER THE BED. I'VE GOT A BRAND NEW TOY FOR YOU.
UH OH. I THINK I SAW A TENTACLE UNDER THE BED!
MONSTERS!
TURN ON THE LIGHTS! THAT MAKES MONSTERS SHRIVEL UP.
GOOD IDEA.
CLICK!
AARRGHHH! AIEEEE AAHHHHHH!! GAACKK
HA HA. WE GOT 'EM!
JUST THE ONES UNDER THE BED. WE'D BETTER OPEN UP THE DRAWERS AND CLOSET TOO, AND GET SOME LIGHT IN THOSE PLACES!
BY GOLLY, NO MONSTERS ARE GOING TO GET US TONIGHT! WITHER AND DIE, BLOODSUCKING FREAKS OF NATURE!!
WHY IS YOUR LIGHT ON? WHAT IN THE WORLD ARE YOU DOING?!?
MONSTERS, DAD. THEY COULD BE ANYWHERE.
YOU'RE TRASHING YOUR ROOM AT 1:00 IN THE MORNING, LOOKING FOR MONSTERS?! IF YOU DON'T GET IN BED THIS INSTANT, YOU'LL HAVE A LOT MORE TO WORRY ABOUT THAN STUPID MONSTERS!!
...WHAT WE NEED IS SOME WAY TO SHRIVEL HIM UP.
WATTERSON

HEY CALVIN, WHATCHA DOIN'?
SHHH!
QUIET DOWN OR YOU'LL GIVE AWAY MY POSITION. HOBBES AND I ARE HAVING A WATER FIGHT.
A WATER FIGHT! CAN I PLAY?
YOU? HA! WAR IS A **MANLY** ART!
I SUPPOSE ANYTHING SO IDIOTIC WOULD **HAVE** TO BE. CAN I PLAY IN YOUR GAME OR NOT?
I DON'T KNOW, IT SEEMS YOU'D RATHER BE MAKING SMART REMARKS.
WATTERSON

C'MON, CAN'T I JOIN YOUR WATER FIGHT? I HAVE MY OWN WATER PISTOL AND EVERYTHING! IT'LL JUST TAKE ME A MINUTE TO GET IT.
OK, YOU CAN PLAY, BUT HOBBES IS ON **MY** TEAM. YOU HAVE TO FIGHT BOTH OF US.
WATTERSON
GREAT! I CAN BEAT YOU AND YOUR STUFFED TIGER ANY DAY. I'LL GO PUT ON MY SWIMSUIT.
SUSIE'S GOING TO PLAY WITH US, OK?
OH BOY. GIRLS FLIP FOR GUYS IN JAMS.

I GOT MY WATER PISTOL! I'M ALL SET!
GOOD. NOW HOBBES AND I WILL BE ONE TEAM, AND YOU...
LOOK AT YOUR TOY TIGER! HE'S WEARING **JAMS**!! THAT'S SO **CUTE**! LET ME SQUEEZE HIM!
WATTERSON
OH FOR PETE'S SAKE, KNOCK IT OFF! YOU GO AROUND THE HOUSE AND COUNT TO FIFTY, AND THEN WE BEGIN, ALL RIGHT?
YOU AND YOUR DUMB JAMS. THIS IS **WAR**, REMEMBER?!
YOU'RE JUST JEALOUS. ...OOH, WHAT A BABE!

LISTEN UP, YOGURT BRAIN. HERE'S OUR STRATEGY: I'LL GO AROUND THE HOUSE **THIS** WAY, AND YOU GO AROUND THE **OTHER** WAY.
I'LL DRAW SUSIE'S FIRE, AND YOU CAN LET HER HAVE IT FROM BEHIND WITH YOUR WATER BALLOON!
GOT IT? OK, LET'S GO!
THANKS FOR THE WATER BALLOON, HOBBES. YOU'RE A GREAT DOUBLE AGENT!
WATTERSON

HA HA! AMBUSH!! HAVE A DRINK, SUSIE!
WHOA! WHOOP! YOU'VE GOT HOBBES' WATER BALLOON! WHERE DID...? HOW...? ..UH OH..
BLOOSH!
I PROMISE YOU YOU'LL HANG FOR THIS, TRAITOR!
I'M EASILY WILED BY A WOMAN IN A SWIMSUIT.
WATTERSON

MY BEST FRIEND BETRAYS ME! SUSIE DRENCHED ME WITH MY OWN TEAMMATE'S WATER BALLOON!
SOME BUDDY *YOU* ARE, YOU BENEDICT ARNOLD!
HMPH. I'D DO IT AGAIN IN A MINUTE. SUSIE LIKES MY JAMS.
DON'T EVEN TALK TO ME! YOU AND I ARE THROUGH!
HA! PROMISES, PROMISES!
UM... I TAKE IT THE GAME IS OVER.
GET THIS TRAITOR OFF ME. HE CHEATS WHEN HE FIGHTS, TOO.
WATTERSON

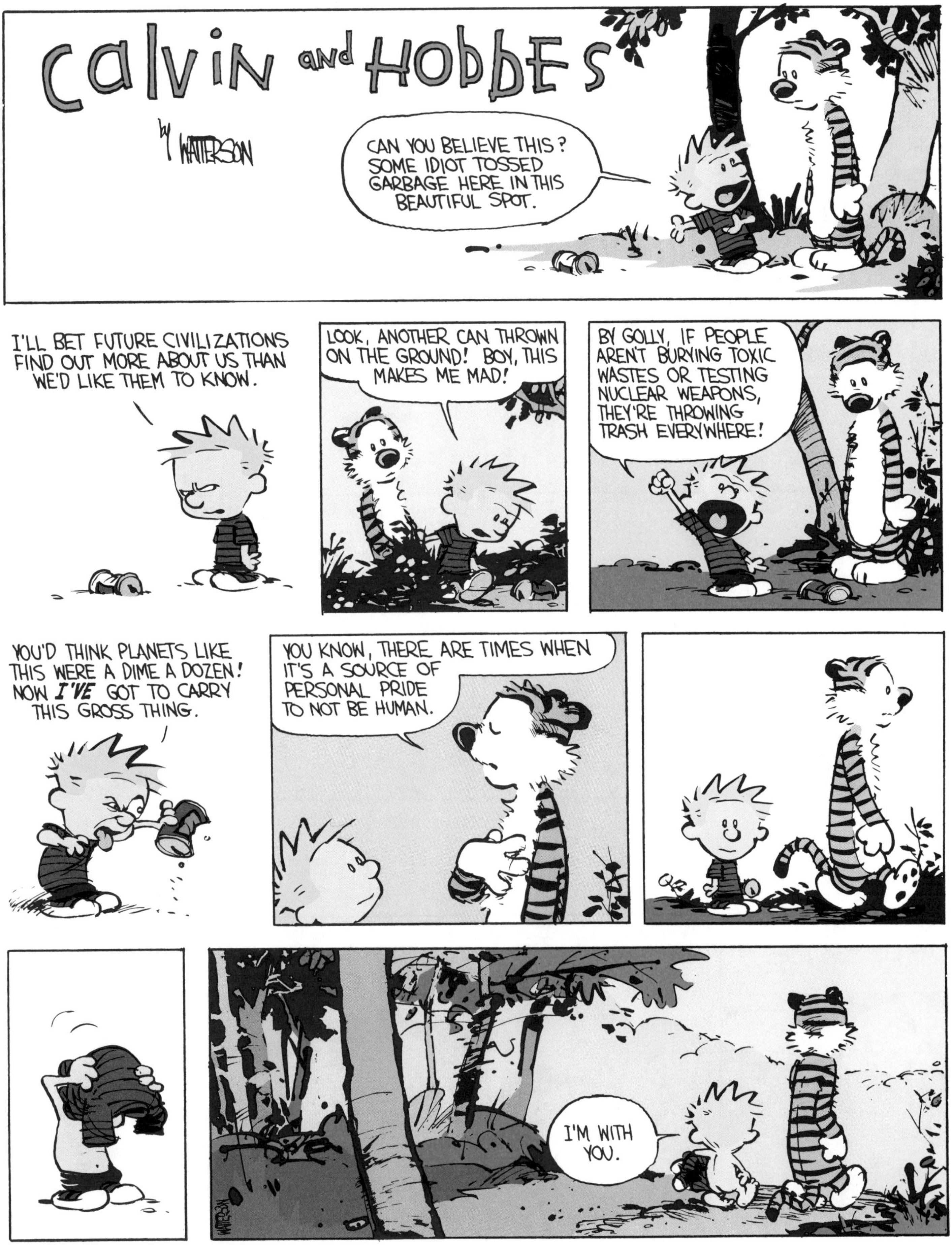
Calvin and HOBBES
by WATTERSON
CAN YOU BELIEVE THIS? SOME IDIOT TOSSED GARBAGE HERE IN THIS BEAUTIFUL SPOT.
I'LL BET FUTURE CIVILIZATIONS FIND OUT MORE ABOUT US THAN WE'D LIKE THEM TO KNOW.
LOOK, ANOTHER CAN THROWN ON THE GROUND! BOY, THIS MAKES ME MAD!
BY GOLLY, IF PEOPLE AREN'T BURYING TOXIC WASTES OR TESTING NUCLEAR WEAPONS, THEY'RE THROWING TRASH EVERYWHERE!
YOU'D THINK PLANETS LIKE THIS WERE A DIME A DOZEN! NOW *I'VE* GOT TO CARRY THIS GROSS THING.
YOU KNOW, THERE ARE TIMES WHEN IT'S A SOURCE OF PERSONAL PRIDE TO NOT BE HUMAN.
I'M WITH YOU.
WATTERSON

AREN'T THESE LONG SUMMER DAYS GREAT? NO RESPONSIBILITIES AT ALL! WE HAVE THE WHOLE DAY TO OURSELVES.
DON'T YOU WISH IT COULD BE LIKE THIS ALL YEAR, FOREVER? NO SCHOOL, NO JOB, NO ANYTHING?
!
YEAH, JUST GLOAT ABOUT IT, WHY DON'T YOU!!
WATTERSON

HEY DAD, WHAT ARE CLOUDS MADE OF?
HMM... I USED TO KNOW THAT. I THINK THEY'RE MOSTLY WATER.
SO HOW COME THEY FLOAT?
WELL, IT'S SORT OF EVAPORATED WATER. MAYBE THERE ARE SOME OTHER GASES, TOO. I'M NOT SURE.
WATTERSON
SO WHY ARE THEY WHITE WHEN THE REST OF THE SKY IS BLUE?
HECK, BEATS ME. I GUESS WE OUGHT TO LOOK THIS STUFF UP.
I TAKE IT THERE'S NO QUALIFYING EXAM TO BE A DAD.

ONE OF THE BEST THINGS ABOUT SUMMER IS GOING TO SLEEP WITH THE FAN ON.
THE GENTLE BREEZE BLOWING, THE DRONING HUM...EVERYTHING SEEMS SAFE AND SERENE WHEN THE FAN IS ON.
IT'S COOL AND LULLING AND PERFECT FOR SLEEP.
WATTERSON
IT ALMOST LETS ONE FORGET HE HAS A HEAVY FUR COAT FOR A BUNKMATE.
IF YOU DON'T LIKE IT, THERE'S PLENTY OF ROOM ON THE FLOOR, BUSTER.

HEY MOM, WHAT'S THIS I HEAR ABOUT THE GREENHOUSE EFFECT?
THEY SAY THE POLLUTANTS WE DUMP IN THE AIR ARE TRAPPING IN THE SUN'S HEAT AND IT'S GOING TO MELT THE POLAR ICE CAPS!
SURE, YOU'LL BE GONE WHEN IT HAPPENS, BUT I WON'T! NICE PLANET YOU'RE LEAVING ME!
WATTERSON
THIS FROM THE KID WHO WANTS TO BE CHAUFFEURED ANY PLACE MORE THAN A BLOCK AWAY.
HEY, NOBODY TOLD ME ABOUT THE ICE CAPS, ALL RIGHT?

MORE BAD NEWS ON YOUR POLLS, DAD. WE'RE LOOKING AT AN ALL-TIME LOW IN POPULARITY HERE.
WELL, CALVIN, THAT'S CERTAINLY FOOD FOR THOUGHT.
NOW HERE'S SOMETHING YOU CAN THINK ABOUT. THE AVERAGE COST OF RAISING A KID TO AGE 18 IS $100,000. THAT'S A LOT OF MONEY.
SO THE QUESTION YOU SHOULD BE ASKING YOURSELF IS, "IS THAT HUNDRED GRAND A GIFT... OR A LOAN?"
GOTCHA, DAD. I WAS JUST ON MY WAY TO BED.

RING RING
HELLO?
MAY I SPEAK WITH YOUR FATHER, PLEASE?
HECK, YOU DON'T NEED MY PERMISSION! BE MY GUEST!
WHAT A WEIRDO.
RING RING
WATTERSON

Calvin and HOBBES
by WATTERSON
TIGERS ARE NATURAL-BORN TREE CLIMBERS.
THAT'S IT, YOU CLIMB UP AND THEN HELP ME UP!
OF COURSE, WE USUALLY HAVE GRAPPLING HOOKS, ROPES AND UTILITY BELTS.
HEY, HERE'S A GREAT TREE FOR CLIMBING! LET ME GET ON YOUR SHOULDERS SO I CAN REACH THE FIRST BRANCH, OK?
GEEZ, HOW MANY BRICKS DO YOU HAVE IN YOUR POCKETS?!
WHOA! HOLD STEADY, YOU WEAKLING!
I'VE ALMOST GOT IT! MOVE UP, MOVE UP!
HURRY AND GRAB IT BEFORE MY SPINE TELESCOPES.
WATTERSON
GOT IT! ...HEY, DON'T LET GO! HOLD ME UP!
FORGET IT! YOU CAN SUPPORT YOUR OWN WEIGHT, BOWLING BALL BUTT.
MMPH! MMPH! I CAN'T GET UP! GIVE ME A BOOST!
HEY! WHAT ARE YOU DOING?! DONT TAKE OFF MY SHOES!
ARE YOU NUTS? HEY, STOP!
AACK! OH NO! DON'T TICKLE! PBTH! EEK! HEE HEE HA HA! STOP IT! I CAN'T HOLD ON!
HEE HEE HOO HOO
AAUGH!
NICE LANDING. I'M PROBABLY PARALYZED.
ALL EXCEPT YOUR MOUTH, OBVIOUSLY. I'M NOT SORRY AT ALL. GIVE ME BACK MY SHOES.
NO.

I CAN'T BELIEVE HOW DULL MY LIFE IS. IT'S SO BORING HERE.
NOTHING EVER CHANGES AROUND HERE. NOTHING EVER HAPPENS.
IT SEEMS AS IF (HANG ON) EVERYBODY BUT ME GETS TO HAVE AN EXCITING LIFE.
ACTUALLY, I'D LIKE **LESS** EXCITEMENT IN MY LIFE.
WHY? ARE YOU DOING FUN THINGS WHEN I'M NOT AROUND?? HUH? **ARE** YOU ?!

WHAT'S WRONG, CALVIN? WHY ARE YOU STILL IN BED?
I DON'T FEEL GOOD.
YOUR FOREHEAD SEEMS WARM. WE'D BETTER TAKE YOUR TEMPERATURE.
I CAN'T BE SICK **NOW!** IT'S STILL SUMMER VACATION! THERE'S NO SCHOOL TO STAY HOME FROM! THIS IS **MY** TIME!
SOMEBODY OWES ME BIG FOR THIS!!

HI THERE, CALVIN. I UNDERSTAND YOU'RE NOT FEELING WELL.
ME? I'M FINE! I JUST SIT AROUND TORTURE CHAMBERS IN MY UNDERWEAR FOR KICKS. LET'S SEE YOUR DEGREE, YOU QUACK!
I'M NOT GOING TO HURT YOU. I'M JUST GOING TO EXAMINE YOU TO SEE WHAT'S WRONG.
I'LL TELL YOU WHAT'S WRONG! I'VE GOT DR. FRANKENSTEIN FOR A PEDIATRICIAN, **THAT'S** WHAT'S WRONG!
NURSE, CALL THE ANESTHESIOLOGIST IN HERE, WILL YOU PLEASE?
MY DAD'S A LAWYER, I'LL HAVE YOU KNOW! DON'T COME NEAR ME!

DEEP IN A DANK DUNGEON ON THE DISMAL PLANET ZOG, THE FEARLESS SPACEMAN SPIFF IS HELD PRISONER BY THE SINISTER ZOG KING.
A GUARD LEADS SPIFF TO THE INTERROGATION ROOM. OUR HERO IS STOIC AND DEFIANT!
AT LAST I MEET THE FAMED SPACEMAN SPIFF! I TRUST YOU ARE...HEH HEH... ENJOYING YOUR VISIT?
YOU'RE WASTING YOUR TIME, MAGGOT FROM MARS! I'LL NEVER GIVE IN!
NEVER, YOU HEAR ME?! NEVER!
KID, DON'T MAKE ME RECANT THE HIPPOCRATIC OATH, OK?

WELL, YOU CERTAINLY WERE A TERROR IN THE DOCTOR'S OFFICE.
I FENDED HIM OFF WITH HIS OWN TONGUE DEPRESSOR. THAT'S WHY I DIDN'T GET A SHOT.
YOU DIDN'T NEED A SHOT. YOUR BEHAVIOR WAS INEXCUSABLE.
ALL THAT COUNTS IS THAT HE COULDN'T GET NEAR ENOUGH TO STICK ME. HE THINKS I'M A LITTLE PINK PIN CUSHION IN UNDERPANTS.
SOMEDAY I HOPE YOU HAVE A KID THAT PUTS YOU THROUGH WHAT I'VE GONE THROUGH.
YEAH, GRANDMA SAYS THAT'S WHAT SHE USED TO TELL YOU.

HERE IS A PROUD CITY, FULL OF HAPPY, PROSPEROUS CITIZENS.
THEY GO ON ABOUT THEIR BUSINESS, UNAWARE THAT THE MOON HAS MYSTERIOUSLY MOVED A FEW MILES CLOSER TO THE EARTH.
...UNAWARE, THAT IS, UNTIL THE TIDE COMES IN.
SPLOOSH!
GISSHHH!

Calvin and HOBBES
by WATTERSON
THE FIRE'S NOT LIGHTING, HUH? CAN I MAKE A SUGGESTION?
LIGHTER FLUID
GIVE UP ON THAT SISSY LIGHTER FLUID.
GASOLINE
DANGER
CAN'T WE COOK THE HAMBURGERS YET?
THE COALS AREN'T HOT ENOUGH.
BUT I'M HUNGRY! I WANT TO EAT NOW!
WELL, YOU'LL JUST HAVE TO WAIT.
YOU KNOW, CALVIN, SOMETIMES THE ANTICIPATION OF SOMETHING IS MORE FUN THAN THE THING ITSELF ONCE YOU GET IT.
HERE WE ARE, IT'S A BEAUTIFUL EVENING. IT'S NICE TO JUST SIT HERE AND LOOK AT THE TREES WHILE WE WAIT FOR THE COALS TO GET HOT, DON'T YOU THINK?
DINNER WILL BE OVER SOON, AND AFTERWARD WE'LL BE DISTRACTED WITH OTHER THINGS TO DO. BUT NOW WE HAVE A FEW MINUTES TO OURSELVES TO ENJOY THE EVENING.
THESE SUMMER DAYS GO BY SO QUICKLY. IT'S GOOD THAT EVERY NOW AND THEN WE HAVE TO WAIT FOR SOMETHING.
SO SHOULD I GO TO McDONALD'S THEN, OR WHAT?
YEAH, I KNOW. YOU THINK YOU'RE GOING TO BE SIX ALL YOUR LIFE.
WATTERSON

WATTERSON

WHAT A PERFECT DAY!
ISN'T IT GREAT TO BE ON SUMMER VACATION? TO BE ABLE TO ENJOY ALL THIS WITH NO SCHOOL AND NO RESPONSIBILITIES?
..AHHHHHHH...
I CAN'T BELIEVE THERE'S NOTHING ON TV BUT REPEATS.
WATTERSON

I THINK A BEE LANDED ON MY BACK! CAN YOU SEE IT? I DON'T WANT TO MOVE!
THAT'S NOT A BEE.
IT ISN'T? *WHEW*
NO, THAT'S A HORNET IF I EVER SAW ONE!
OW!
WATTERSON

Calvin and HOBBES
by WATTERSON
WIPE THAT GRIN OFF YOUR FACE!
WELL, HOBBES, HOW DO I LOOK?
I'M DOING MY BEST TO BITE MY TONGUE.
I CUT OUT CONSTRUCTION PAPER FEATHERS AND TAPED THEM ON MY ARMS SO I CAN FLY! PRETTY NEAT, HUH?
IF PAPER FEATHERS ARE ALL IT TAKES TO FLY, DON'T YOU THINK WE'D HAVE HEARD ABOUT IT BEFORE?
IT TAKES AN UNCOMMON MIND TO THINK OF THESE THINGS, HOBBES.
I'D AGREE WITH THAT.
HERE'S A GORGE. THIS IS A GOOD SPOT.
YOU'RE GOING TO JUMP OFF THIS LEDGE?
HECK NO! I NEED MOMENTUM! I WANT YOU TO TOSS ME OVER.
YOU UNDERSTAND I ASSUME NO RESPONSIBILITY FOR THIS?
RIGHT. I GET THE PATENT.
HEAVE!
I'M FLYING! I'M FLYING!
I'M..... UH OH...
WATTERSON
DON'T SELL THE BIKE SHOP, ORVILLE.
SHUT UP AND GO GET ME SOME ANTISEPTIC.

Calvin and Hobbes
by WATTERSON
THAT RUN DOESN'T COUNT! YOU DIDN'T TOUCH THIRD BASE!
THAT'S 'CAUSE THIRD BASE CRAWLED TO THE OUTFIELD!
WAP!
WATTERSON
HA HA! EASY OUT!!
HEY! WHERE ARE YOU GOING?!
EEEEEEE
YOU HAVE TO STAY ON THE BASE LINE, YOU CHEATER!
YEAH? PROVE IT!
THIS ISN'T FAIR! YOU CAN'T RUN ANYWHERE!
JUST WATCH ME!
IF WE HAD A FIRST BASEMAN, YOU'D'VE BEEN OUT LONG AGO!
BUT WE DON'T, DO WE?
GOTCHA! YOU'RE OUT!
OK, I'M UP TO BAT AGAIN! WHAT FUN! TWO-MAN BASEBALL IS A REAL SPORT!
A REAL SPORT FOR IDIOTS. NEXT TIME I'M GOING TO TAG YOU OUT WITH THE BAT INSTEAD OF THE BALL.

HOBBES, DID YOU HEAR? MOM AND DAD ARE TAKING US CAMPING!
WE GET TO LIVE IN A TENT AND GO FISHING AND CANOEING! WON'T THAT BE **FUN**??
WATTERSON
WE'LL BE ROUGHING IT! LIVING OFF THE LAND! NO TV OR RADIO OR....
UH-OH.
WHAT'S WRONG?
THIS SOUNDS SUSPICIOUSLY LIKE ONE OF DAD'S PLOTS TO BUILD MY CHARACTER.

GOSH, THIS IS GOING TO BE A **FUN** VACATION! CAMPING OUT! WOW!
WATTERSON
I CAN'T WAIT TO GET THERE! A WHOLE WEEK OF HIKING AND CANOEING AND SWIMMING AND FISHING!
A WHOLE WEEK WITHOUT A SINGLE NEWSPAPER OR A DECENT CUP OF REAL COFFEE.
DOESN'T MOM **LIKE** CAMPING?
MOM WAS UP A LITTLE TOO LATE PACKING.

SEE THAT ISLAND UP AHEAD? THAT'S WHERE WE'RE CAMPING!
OH BOY!
AHH, THIS IS THE LIFE! FRESH AIR, CLEAN WATER, LOTS OF EXERCISE, AND...
BOOM!
WATTERSON
DEAR, YOU'RE BACK-PADDLING.
WE'RE TURNING AROUND AND FINDING A HOTEL!

WHEN'S THIS RAIN GOING TO LET UP?
I DON'T KNOW, CALVIN.
HEY, CHEER UP, GANG! I PACKED STORM GEAR. "ALWAYS BE PREPARED," YOU KNOW.
THESE PONCHOS ARE SUPER. THEY'RE THERMAL-SEALED LIGHTWEIGHT NYLON, LAMINATED WITH FLEXIBLE URETHANE FOR COMPLETE WATER PROTECTION!
YEAH, DAD. IT'S GREAT THAT WE WON'T GET WETTER THAN WE ALREADY ARE.
ZINC OXIDE, THONGS, TANNING LOTION... WRONG DUFFEL BAG. LET'S SEE, WHICH ONE OF THESE WAS IT?

I'M GLAD DAD FINALLY GOT THE TENTS UP. NOW I CAN GET OUT OF THESE SOGGY CLOTHES.
TOO BAD YOU CAN'T PUT ON DRY CLOTHES. YOU'D FEEL A LOT BETTER.
HEY, WAIT! NO! DON'T DO THAT HERE!!
ACKPTH!

SOME TROUPER YOU ARE! WHAT'S A LITTLE RAIN? THIS IS WHAT BEING IN THE WILDERNESS IS ALL ABOUT!
HA HA! AT LEAST IT'S NOT SNOWING, RIGHT?
RIGHT?
I MEAN, SAY IT WAS SNOWING SO HARD WE COULDN'T MAKE A FIRE.
BOY, I LOVE COLD CANNED RAVIOLI.

Calvin and HOBBES
by WATTERSON
TUM DE TA TA DEE DEE DO
BOY, THIS SURE BEATS SITTING IN AN OFFICE ALL DAY!
IS IT STILL RAINING?
OF COURSE IT'S STILL RAINING. IT'S BEEN RAINING FOR DAYS. WHY SHOULD IT STOP NOW?!
WE'RE GOING TO NEED A VACATION AFTER THIS VACATION.
I'LL SAY! WE CAN'T EVEN KEEP A FIRE GOING.
I CAN'T BELIEVE DAD WENT OUT TO CATCH FISH.
IN THIS WEATHER? HE'S A FANATIC!
EITHER THAT, OR WE'RE ALL OUT OF PACKAGED FOOD. WE'LL PROBABLY STARVE TO DEATH ON THIS GOD-FORSAKEN ROCK.
AFTER ALL THAT SPAM, STARVING DOESN'T SOUND SO BAD.
IF WE LIVE TO GET HOME, I'M NEVER GOING TO SET FOOT OUTSIDE AGAIN AS LONG AS I LIVE.
WHAT A LUCKY KID CALVIN IS! I NEVER GOT TO DO THIS STUFF WHEN I WAS HIS AGE!
HEY CALVIN! WANT TO LEARN HOW TO GUT A FISH?
WATTERSON

HOW'S THE WATER?
FREEZING. I'M COMING OUT. HAND ME MY TOWEL, OK?
WRING WRING
THIS IS THE DUMBEST VACATION I'VE EVER BEEN ON.

IT HASN'T BEEN VERY BUGGY THIS WEEK, HAS IT?
YOU'RE REALLY REACHING, DAD.

WE'RE PACKING UP?
YEP. I'VE HAD ENOUGH. WHAT A ROTTEN WEEK!
WAP
DID YOU KNOW WHAT ANY OF DAD'S WORDS MEANT?
NO, BUT I WROTE THEM DOWN SO WE CAN LOOK 'EM UP WHEN WE GET HOME.

WELL, GANG, I'M SORRY THE WEATHER WASN'T ANY BETTER THIS WEEK.
I KNOW IT WASN'T ALWAYS A LOT OF FUN, BUT WE LIVED THROUGH IT, AND WE GOT TO SPEND SOME TIME TOGETHER, AND THAT'S WHAT'S REALLY IMPORTANT.
ANYWAY, I HOPE YOU'RE ALL NOT **TOO** DISAPPOINTED.
CALVIN, TELL YOUR DAD ANY JUDGE WOULD TAKE THIS TRIP AS GROUNDS FOR DIVORCE.
DAD, MOM SAYS...
ALL RIGHT! ALL RIGHT!

DAD, CAN YOU GET MY BALL OUT OF THE GUTTER AGAIN?
THIS IS THE THIRD TIME THIS AFTERNOON! I THOUGHT I TOLD YOU TO PLAY OUT BACK!
RELAX, DAD. IT'S JUST A BALL IN THE GUTTER. IT'S NOT AS IF I'VE BEEN EMBEZZLING MONEY OR KILLING PEOPLE, RIGHT? AREN'T YOU GLAD I'M NOT STEALING AND MURDERING?
I ALWAYS HAVE TO HELP DAD ESTABLISH THE PROPER CONTEXT.

C'MON, HOBBES. LET DOWN THE ROPE LADDER.
WHAT'S THE REST OF THE PASSWORD?
I THINK FIVE VERSES EXTOLLING TIGERS IS **PLENTY**. YOU KNOW IT'S ME! LET ME UP!
NO.
OOH, WHY YOU LOUSY, ROTTEN, STINKING..
IF YOU CALL ME NAMES, YOU HAVE TO START OVER AT THE BEGINNING.
VERSE SIX: "TIGERS ARE NIMBLE AND LIGHT ON THEIR TOES, MY ***RE***SPECT FOR TIGERS CONTINUALLY GROWS."
YOU'RE NOT DOING THE DANCE.

Calvin and HOBBES
by WATTERSON
AH-CHOO!
WHEW ...NO BRAINS.
AH.. AH.. AH.. AH
CHOOOO!!
THE FORCE OF THE NASAL EXPLOSION SENDS CALVIN REELING THROUGH THE STRATOSPHERE!
WITH LESS AND LESS AIR TO RESIST HIS MOMENTUM, HE BREAKS THE PULL OF EARTH'S GRAVITY AND HURLS PAST THE MOON!
AS HE PASSES OUT OF THE GALAXY, CALVIN REFLECTS ON THE WISDOM OF COVERING ONE'S MOUTH WHEN SNEEZING TO DEFLECT THE PROPULSION.
ALAS, IT IS KNOWLEDGE GAINED TOO LATE FOR POOR CALVIN, THE HUMAN SATELLITE! ...BUT WAIT! ANOTHER SNEEZE IS BREWING! CALVIN TURNS HIMSELF AROUND!
THE SECOND SNEEZE ROCKETS HIM BACK TO EARTH! HE'S SAVED! IT'S A MIRACLE!
AH CHOO!
GOD BLESS YOU.
OH, HE DOES, MOM. HE DOES.
WATTERSON

THE END OF SUMMER IS ALWAYS HARD ON ME.
...TRYING TO CRAM IN ALL THE GOOFING OFF I'VE BEEN MEANING TO DO.
WATTERSON

HOW COME YOU'RE STILL HOME? WHY AREN'T YOU AT WORK?
I TOOK THE DAY OFF.
WATTERSON
SAY, DAD, CAN I HAVE A LOOK AT THE CLASSIFIED SECTION?
AS SOON AS I'M THROUGH WITH IT.
GOSH, DAD, I'D SURE LIKE TO BORROW THAT SECTION RIGHT THIS MINUTE.
WHY DON'T YOU READ THE EDITORIALS?
"NEW DAD WANTED. FREQUENT TRAVELER PREFERRED. LIBERAL VIEWS ON DISCIPLINE A MUST. ASK FOR CALVIN DURING NORMAL WORK HOURS."

I DON'T WANNA TAKE A BATH! I HATE TAKING BATHS!
AAAAAAAAAAAAA
NO NO NO NO NO NO NO NO NO NO NO NO NO NO NO NO NO NO NO
WATTERSON
THEY CAN MAKE ME DO IT, BUT THEY CAN'T MAKE ME DO IT WITH DIGNITY.

RATS. I CAN'T TELL MY GUM FROM MY SILLY PUTTY.

WAP WAP WAP WAP
WIPPITY WAPPITY WIPPITY WAPPITY
BIPPITABIPPITABIPPITABIPPITABIPPITA

I'M NEVER GONNA GET MARRIED. ARE YOU?
HMM... I SUPPOSE IF THE RIGHT PERSON CAME ALONG, I MIGHT.
SOMEBODY WITH GREEN EYES AND A NICE LAUGH, WHO I COULD CALL "POOTY PIE."
"POOTY PIE"?!?
OR "BITSY POOKUMS."
I THINK THAT WOULD AFFECT MY STOMACH A LOT MORE THAN MY HEART.
"BITSY POOKUMS," I'D SAY. "YES, SNOOGY WOOGY," SHE'D REPLY...

Calvin and HOBBES
by WATTERSON
STIR STIR
STRETTCCHHH
STAB STAB
PAT PAT PAT
MUSH MUSH
SNIFF
HWOOF!
LICK
ACKPTGH
BLECHH
GLUG GLUG GLUG
SMACK
BR-R-R-R-R
HAAAKK HOCCHH
CHOKE... GASP...
THERE...(PANT)... SEE? I...I... TRIED IT. (COUGH) IT... ALMOST (WHEEZE) KILLED... ME.
CLAP CLAP CLAP CLAP CL
ENCORE.
BRAVO.
I'M GOING TO RUN AWAY TO ALASKA.
WATTERSON

WANT TO GO TIME TRAVELING WITH ME?
SEE, I BUILT A TIME MACHINE.
TIME MACHIN
THIS LOOKS LIKE YOUR TRANSMOGRIFIER.
TO THE INATTENTIVE AND BRAINLESS LAYMAN, YES. BUT YOU CRAWL **UNDER** THE TRANSMOGRIFIER, WHEREAS WITH THE TIME MACHINE, YOU CLIMB IN THE **TOP**.
AHH..

ARE WE GOING TO TRAVEL INTO THE PAST OR INTO THE FUTURE?
WELL, I SUPPOSE IF WE WENT INTO THE PAST, I COULD ACE ANY UPCOMING HISTORY EXAMS IN SCHOOL. THAT MIGHT BE USEFUL.
BUT IF WE WENT INTO THE FUTURE, WE COULD SWIPE SOMETHING AND PRETEND TO INVENT IT WHEN WE GOT BACK. WE COULD BE RICH.
THE FUTURE IT IS, THEN!
RIGHT. ONCE I'M RICH, I CAN ***HIRE*** SOMEBODY TO TAKE ALL MY DUMB TESTS!
TIME MACHINE

OK, HOBBES, OUR TIME MACHINE IS ALL SET. PUT ON YOUR GOGGLES AND WE'LL BE OFF TO THE FUTURE!
TIME MACHINE
WHY DO WE HAVE TO WEAR GOGGLES?
GEEZ, DO YOU THINK TRAVELING YEARS INTO THE FUTURE IS LIKE DRIVING DOWN THE STREET?!
WE'VE GOT TO CONTEND WITH VORTEXES AND LIGHT SPEEDS! ANYTHING COULD GO WRONG! OF COURSE WE NEED TO WEAR GOGGLES!
GOSH, I THINK MY GOGGLES ARE IN THE BEDROOM. IF I'M NOT BACK IN A COUPLE MINUTES, YOU CAN GO WITHOUT ME.
SIT DOWN, SISSY. I ALREADY GOT YOUR GOGGLES.
MACHINE

ALL READY? I'LL JUST PUSH THE BUTTON AND OFF WE GO INTO THE FUTURE!
TIME MACHINE
UP, UP AND AWAAYYY!
WE'RE APPROACHING LIGHT SPEED, HOBBES! HANG ON!
I HAVE TO GO TO THE BATHROOM.
NOW?!
IN HYPERSPACE?! ARE YOU CRAZY?!?

WHAT YEAR IN THE FUTURE ARE WE GOING TO LAND?
TIME MACHINE
IT'S HARD TO PINPOINT EXACTLY, BUT I'D SAY SOMETIME AROUND THE TURN OF THE CENTURY.
I HOPE OL' EARTH IS STILL AROUND THEN. I'VE GROWN FOND OF IT.
IF NOT, WE'LL RETURN TO THE PRESENT AND SEE IF DAD WILL GIVE ME MY COLLEGE TUITION EARLY IN CASH.
TIME MACHINE

HANG ON! WE'RE COMING IN!
SCREEEEECHHH
WOW! SO THIS IS THE FUTURE!
I KINDA PICTURED MORE BUILDINGS.
MAYBE WE LANDED IN AN ARBORETUM.

LET'S HAVE A LOOK AROUND. I'M SURE WE'LL RUN INTO A ROBOT OR SOMETHING.
TIME MACHINE
LOOK AT THIS.
GOSH, I WONDER WHAT FUTURISTIC DEVICE THIS IS! SOME SORT OF TRANSPORTATION POD, I'D GUESS.
I WONDER HOW YOU GET IN?
I DON'T SEE A DOOR OR LICENSE NUMBER ANYWHERE.
THIS IS VERY PECULIAR.
HAVE YOU EVER SEEN A TREE THIS COLOR?

I MUST SAY, THE FUTURE IS QUITE A BIT DIFFERENT THAN I EXPECTED.
THIS BREEZE IS SO HOT AND MUGGY. I FIGURED THEY'D BE ABLE TO CONTROL THE WEATHER BY NOW.
THE AIR STINKS, TOO. I GUESS THERE'S STILL POLLUTION.
EVER FEEL AS IF YOU'RE BEING MONITORED?
...OR THAT YOU'RE ABOUT TO DO A DOUBLE-TAKE?

AAUGH
BACK TO THE TIME MACHINE!
RUN!
WE MUST'VE GONE BACK IN TIME INSTEAD OF FORWARD!
WHAT TIPPED YOU OFF? THE DINOSAUR?!
DON'T GET SMART, FUZZBRAIN. JUST GET IN AND FACE THE OTHER DIRECTION SO WE GO INTO THE FUTURE THIS TIME!
YOU MEAN WE WENT INTO THE PAST BECAUSE WE WERE FACING THE WRONG WAY?!?
YOU THINK I'VE GOT SOME TRIPLE-A MAP?! MAYBE YOU'D LIKE TO STEER THIS TIME!

WE MADE IT! IT'S A GOOD THING THE TIME MACHINE DIDN'T STALL, OR WE'D HAVE BEEN EATEN BY DINOSAURS!
WE'RE COMING BACK TOWARD THE PRESENT NOW. DO YOU WANT TO STOP AT HOME, OR KEEP GOING INTO THE FUTURE LIKE WE PLANNED?
I'VE HAD ENOUGH TIME TRAVELING LET'S GO HOME.
LET'S GO JUST A *LITTLE* INTO THE FUTURE AND SEE WHAT I'M LIKE AS A TEEN-AGER!
LET'S NOT, ALL RIGHT?

HI, MOM. HOBBES AND I WENT TIME TRAVELING AND VISITED THE JURASSIC PERIOD TODAY.
THAT'S NICE. WHAT'S IT LIKE?
PRETTY SCARY. A DINOSAUR ALMOST ATE US.
ACTUALLY, WE WERE TRYING TO GO INTO THE FUTURE, BUT WE MADE A MISTAKE.
I SEE. WELL, I'M GLAD YOU MADE IT BACK.
YOUR MOM ISN'T FAZED BY MUCH, IS SHE?
IT DEPENDS. SHE DIDN'T TAKE THE FROGS IN THE TOILET SO WELL, REMEMBER?

DAD, LOOK! THE SUN'S SETTING AND IT'S ONLY 3 O'CLOCK!
IT'S NOT 3 O'CLOCK. YOUR WATCH STOPPED.
TIME DOESN'T STOP IF YOUR WATCH STOPS?
NOPE.
PHOOEY. FOR A MOMENT THERE, I THOUGHT I'D GET RICH PATENTING THIS THING.
I'D HAVE BOUGHT ONE.

Calvin and HOBBES
by WATTERSON
YOU KNOW, SOME PEOPLE NEVER GET TO WALK IN A BEAUTIFUL WOODS LIKE THIS.
...WHILE OTHERS OF US FACE THE PROSPECT OF NEVER DOING ANYTHING ELSE.
OH, HUSH. WE'LL FIND OUR WAY HOME.
YOU DON'T REMEMBER ANY OF THIS?
NOPE. WE'RE SURE LOST **THIS** TIME.
IF I HAD KNOWN WE WEREN'T GOING TO FIND OUR WAY HOME, I'D HAVE BROUGHT MY COLORING BOOK.
WE COULD BE OUT HERE FOR MONTHS.
WE'D BETTER FORAGE FOR SHELTER. THIS WILL BE FUN! WE CAN BE MODERN ROBINSON CRUSOES, LIVING OFF THE LAND BY OUR WITS!
WE CAN BE RUGGED EXPLORERS!
YEAH! WE'LL BE FREE FROM ALL THE CONSTRAINTS OF CIVILIZATION! OH BOY!
HEY, ISN'T THAT OUR BACK YARD?
WHY, SO IT IS.
I DON'T CARE **HOW** LONG YOU'LL BE GONE, I'M ONLY MAKING YOU **ONE** SANDWICH.
HOW ABOUT RIFLES, THEN? DO WE HAVE ANY RIFLES?
WATERSON

IF YOU COULD HAVE THREE WISHES GRANTED, WHAT WOULD THEY BE?
JUST THREE WISHES, HUH? HMM... THAT WOULD BE A TOUGH DECISION.
I GUESS I'D HAVE TO THINK ABOUT IT A WHILE.
OOPS! HANG ON.
OK, I KNOW WHAT MY FIRST WISH WOULD BE.

ONE OF NATURE'S UGLIER CREATURES, THE BAT IS A MISUNDERSTOOD MARVEL OF EVOLUTION.
PRODUCING A SERIES OF LOUD, HIGH-PITCHED SQUEAKS, THE BAT CAN JUDGE AN INSECT'S DISTANCE AND ELEVATION BY THE TIME DELAY OF THE SQUEAK'S ECHO!
CHANGES IN THE ECHO'S PITCH REVEAL THE DOOMED BUG'S DIRECTION! NO MOVEMENT ESCAPES THE INCREDIBLE SENSES OF THE BAT!
GLUMP!
TA-DAA! EYES CLOSED!
CALVIN, SIT UP AND EAT WITH A FORK LIKE A CIVILIZED HUMAN BEING.

YAWN
WAAUUGHH!
FOR THE LAST TIME, GET OUT OF BED! WE'RE GOING TO BE LATE.
I'M TRYING. I'M TRYING.

MOM WANTS ME TO CLEAN MY ROOM. THIS IS THE LAST STRAW!
I DON'T HAVE TO PUT UP WITH THIS TOTALITARIANISM! I'M SECEDING!
GEE, CAN YOU SECEDE FROM YOUR OWN FAMILY?
WHY NOT?! I NEVER SIGNED UP FOR THIS GROUP! I WASN'T EVEN CONSULTED!
THE ONLY REASON MOM AND DAD ARE MY PARENTS IS BECAUSE I WAS **BORN** TO THEM!
A BIOLOGICAL CONSPIRACY, HUH?

WE CAN LIVE ANYWHERE WE WANT TO NOW THAT WE'RE SECEDING FROM THE FAMILY!
WHERE DO YOU WANT TO GO? THE SAHARA? ANTARCTICA?
HOW ARE WE GOING TO GET TO ANY OF **THOSE** PLACES? WE DON'T EVEN HAVE A CAR!
OK DAD, FOR **THIS** AMAZING TRICK I'LL NEED AN ORDINARY AMERICAN EXPRESS CARD. NOW CLOSE YOUR EYES...

HOBBES AND I ARE SECEDING FROM THIS FAMILY, MOM.
OH REALLY?
YEP. WE'RE TAKING MY SLED AND MOVING TO THE YUKON.
WELL, **THAT'S** A LONG WAY AWAY.
I KNOW. HERE'S A LIST OF SANDWICHES AND SUPPLIES WE'LL NEED.
WHY SHOULD I DO ALL THIS IF YOU'RE SECEDING FROM THE FAMILY?
WE HAVEN'T SECEDED **YET!** GEEZ, WHAT KIND OF MOM **ARE** YOU?

WELL, I GUESS WE'RE ALL PACKED. COMIC BOOKS, DART GUN, SPACE HELMET AND TOBOGGAN! WE'RE OFF TO THE YUKON!
DO WE HAVE A MAP?
OOH, THAT'S RIGHT! GLAD YOU REMEMBERED! I'LL GO GET ONE!
DON'T WE HAVE ANY ROAD MAPS OF THE YUKON, MOM?
I DOUBT IT.
OK, HERE'S THE YUKON. NOW SEE IF YOU CAN FIND THE UNITED STATES.
HERE THEY ARE! LOOK HOW CLOSE IT IS! THIS WON'T TAKE ANY TIME AT ALL!

SO LONG, "MOM"! WE'RE OFF TO THE YUKON. IT'S BEEN NICE LIVING HERE ... BUT NOT REAL NICE! HA HA!
CALVIN! WAIT A MINUTE.
LEAVE IT TO A MOTHER TO DRAG OUT A GOODBYE. SHEESH.
YOU'RE GOING SOUTHEAST. NORTH IS THAT WAY.
OH YEAH. I KNEW THAT.

THIS SLED IS HEAVY. I THOUGHT WE WERE GOING TO RIDE IT MOST OF THE WAY TO THE YUKON.
WE'VE ONLY BEEN WALKING 20 MINUTES, HOBBES. WE PROBABLY WON'T GET TO NORTHERN CANADA UNTIL THIS AFTERNOON.
IN THAT CASE, I'M TAKING A BREAK.
GOOD IDEA. WANT A COMIC BOOK? HERE'S CAPTAIN NITRO.
I WANT A SANDWICH.
WE JUST HAVE ONE APIECE. WE SHOULD SAVE 'EM IN CASE WE CAN'T CATCH A WALRUS.

Calvin and HobbEs
by WATTERSON
RELAX, HOBBES. THESE SANDWICHES WILL GIVE US ENERGY TO SPARE.
YOU ONLY PACKED TWO SANDWICHES FOR OUR ENTIRE TRIP TO THE YUKON?
MMFF. WHATH THITH? HONEY 'N' MARTHMALLOWTH?
THAT ONE IS. THE OTHER HAS CHOCOLATE SYRUP.
AS LONG AS WE'RE TAKING A BREAK, WE MIGHT AS WELL RECORD OUR PROGRESS IN THE LOG.
"JOURNEY TO THE YUKON: DAY ONE. HAVE TRAVELED TWENTY MINUTES. NO SNOW SO FAR."
"FOOD SUPPLIES LOW."
"NEVERTHELESS, MORALE IS HIGH AS WE PUSH NORTH."
MY MORALE WOULD BE A LOT HIGHER IF YOU'D CARRY THE TOBOGGAN.
ME?! I'M THE LEADER OF THIS EXPEDITION! I'M FORGING THE PATH!
I THINK IT'S MY TURN TO BE LEADER NOW.
YOU CAN'T BE THE LEADER! SEE, I'VE GOT THE COMMANDER HAT.
THAT CAN BE EASILY REMEDIED.
WATTERSON
HEY! LEGGO! THIS IS MY HELMET!
OW! QUIT BITING!
THIS IS MUTINY! GIVE THAT BACK!
I'M THE CAPTAIN NOW. I GIVE THE COMMANDS.
FIRST, I DECREE DOUBLE RATIONS FOR ALL OFFICERS TO AID THEIR DECISION-MAKING CAPABILITIES.
OH NO YOU DON'T!! THAT LAST SANDWICH IS MINE!

I'M NOT GOING TO BE LED BY YOU! I'M THE RIGHTFUL CAPTAIN! YOU JUST STOLE MY CAPTAIN HELMET!
LET'S SAY YOU GAVE IT TO ME UNDER EXTREME DURESS.
OOH, IF YOU WERE LITTLER THAN ME, BOY, I'D POUND YOU!
HA! YOUR MOM TOLD ME YOU HAVE A WEIRD DISEASE AND YOU'RE GOING TO GET SMALLER AS YOU GROW OLDER!
SHE DID NOT! THAT'S NOT TRUE!
IN FACT, SHE'S ALREADY GOT A CONTRACT FROM THE CIRCUS SIDE SHOW. I SAW IT MYSELF.
I'M NOT LISTENING! I'M NOT LISTENING! OHH, SAY CAN YOU SEEEE...
WATTERSON

IF I CAN'T LEAD THE EXPEDITION, I'M NOT GOING AT ALL! YOU CAN GO TO THE YUKON YOURSELF.
HA! AS CAPTAIN, I FIRE YOU ANYWAY!
GOOD! I'M GOING HOME!
YOU DON'T HAVE A HOME. YOU SECEDED, REMEMBER?
MY LIFE NEEDS A REWIND/ERASE BUTTON.
...AND A VOLUME CONTROL.
WATTERSON

WHAT IF MOM AND DAD WON'T TAKE ME BACK BECAUSE I SECEDED? WHAT IF THEY TELL ME I CAN'T REJOIN THE FAMILY?
THEY HAVE TO TAKE ME BACK! I'M THEIR STUPID KID, RIGHT?
WATTERSON
RIGHT!
...THE OPERATIVE WORD BEING "STUPID."

GOSH, MAYBE MOM AND DAD SOLD ALL MY BELONGINGS WHEN I SECEDED.
MAYBE THEY RENTED OUT MY ROOM.
MAYBE THEY *MOVED!*
...A LOT CAN HAPPEN WHEN YOU'RE GONE ALL MORNING!
...MOMMMM!!
WATTERSON
I'M BACK, MOM. I CHANGED MY MIND ABOUT SECEDING. I WANT TO BE YOUR KID AGAIN, OK?
YOU'LL ALWAYS BE MY KID. I'M GLAD YOU'RE BACK.
WELL, HOBBES WAS BEING A MORON, SO I DECIDED I DIDN'T WANT TO LIVE IN THE YUKON WITH HIM.
SO WHERE IS HOBBES NOW?
ISN'T HE BACK YET?
HOW COULD HOBBES GET BACK BY HIMSELF?!
YOU'RE RIGHT. THAT DUMB TIGER COULDN'T FIND HIS WAY OUT OF AN EMPTY ROOM.
WATTERSON
BEDTIME, CALVIN.
WHERE'S HOBBES?
I SUPPOSE HE'S WHEREVER YOU LEFT HIM.
YOU MEAN HE'S STILL IN THE WOODS?! IT'S NIGHT OUT!
WHAT HAVE I TOLD YOU ABOUT LEAVING YOUR BELONGINGS?
HOBBES IS LOST! I'LL GET A FLASHLIGHT! WE'VE GOT TO FIND HIM!
HOBBES! HOBBES!
CALVIN, IT'S YOUR BEDTIME! DON'T YOU PULL THIS STUNT *NOW!*
WATTERSON

Calvin and HOBBES
by WATTERSON
HOBBES, YOU MANGY FUZZ-BRAINED LUNK HEAD, WHERE ARE YOU ?!?
...I DIDN'T MEAN THAT QUITE THE WAY THAT SOUNDED.
C'MON, CALVIN, GET BACK INSIDE. IT'S TOO LATE TO GO SEARCHING FOR YOUR STUFFED TIGER NOW.
I CAN'T LEAVE HOBBES ALONE IN THE WOODS AT NIGHT!
WELL, MAYBE YOU SHOULD HAVE THOUGHT ABOUT THAT BEFORE IT GOT DARK. THIS CAN BE A LITTLE LESSON, HMM?
I THOUGHT HE'D COME BACK BY HIMSELF. I DIDN'T THINK HE'D GET LOST!
WE'LL LOOK FOR HIM TOMORROW. NOW OFF TO BED WITH YOU.
(SNIFF) I HOPE HE'S OK. IF HE HADN'T BEEN ACTING SO STUPID I NEVER WOULD'VE LEFT HIM.
I SURE WISH HE'D COME BACK.
CALVIN LEFT HOBBES SOMEWHERE IN THE WOODS. THE POOR KID'S PRETTY UPSET.
I'LL BET.
I MEAN, HE'S REALLY UPSET.
I SAID I'LL BET HE IS.
REALLY UPSET.
..AHH...
WOULD MY DAD HAVE DONE THIS? OF COURSE NOT. I WAS NEVER SPOILED LIKE THIS...
WATTERSON

NO LUCK?
OF COURSE NOT! HOW AM I GOING TO FIND A STUFFED TIGER IN THE WOODS AT NIGHT?!
WHY CAN'T CALVIN KEEP TRACK OF HIS TOYS?! I MUST BE CRAZY TO BE OUT HERE.
HO-O-OBBES!
OOPS. HEH HEH.
I MAY BE CRAZY, BUT I'M NOT AS CRAZY AS YOU.

IS THAT YOU? DID YOU FIND HOBBES? IT'S ALMOST MIDNIGHT.
YEAH, I GOT HIM. HE WAS OUT THERE WITH THE TOBOGGAN.
OH HONEY, THANK YOU! CALVIN WILL BE SO HAPPY!!
MMF. HE'D BETTER BE, OR TOMORROW I'LL LEAVE HIM IN THE WOODS.
C'MON, WE'LL PUT HOBBES IN CALVIN'S BED SO HE'LL SEE HIM FIRST THING TOMORROW.
Z
HE SNUGGLED UP IN HIS SLEEP! WHAT A LITTLE ANGEL!
ONLY AT NIGHT. I'M GOING TO BED.

HOBBES! YOU'RE BACK! I'M SO GLAD TO SEE YOU!
I'M GLAD TO SEE YOU, TOO.
GOSH, WEREN'T YOU SCARED BEING OUT IN THE WOODS AT NIGHT?
HECK NO, TIGERS AREN'T SCARED OF THAT! I GOT SO BORED I HIKED BACK.
MOM! LOOK! HOBBES IS BACK!
YES, YOUR DAD FOUND HIM LAST NIGHT AND BROUGHT HIM IN.
IS THAT SO-O-O?!
MM-HMM. WHY DON'T YOU GO THANK HIM RIGHT NOW?

HI, CALVIN. I BROUGHT MR. BUN OVER SO WE CAN PLAY HOUSE. YOU AND I CAN BE THE PARENTS, AND HOBBES AND MR. BUN CAN BE OUR CHILDREN.
OH, RIGHT. HOBBES AND I ARE GONNA PUT OUR BIG PLANS ON HOLD SO WE CAN PLAY HOUSE WITH A STUFFED RABBIT? FORGET IT!
I DON'T SEE WHY YOU'LL PLAY WITH YOUR DUMB OL' TIGER AND NOT WITH MR. BUN AND ME! YOU'RE JUST MEAN, THAT'S ALL!
GO PLAY IN A MICROWAVE, SUSIE. WE'RE BUSY.
GIRLS ARE LIKE SLUGS- THEY PROBABLY SERVE SOME PURPOSE, BUT IT'S HARD TO IMAGINE WHAT.
MR. BUN SEEMS COMATOSE. DID YOU NOTICE?
WATTERSON

HI, DAD. I'M REPEATING EVERYTHING ANYONE SAYS.
OH, YOU ARE, ARE YOU?
OH, YOU ARE, ARE YOU?
KNOCK IT OFF, CALVIN. THAT'S VERY ANNOYING.
KNOCK IT OFF, CALVIN. THAT'S VERY ANNOYING.
I FORFEIT ALL MY DESSERTS FOR A WEEK.
OK, GIVE THEM TO **ME**.
HA HA. WHY DON'T YOU GO BOTHER YOUR MOTHER FOR A WHILE?
WATTERSON

WHERE ARE YOU GOING WITH THE TOY TELEPHONE?
OUT IN THE WOODS. YOU CAN COME ALONG IF YOU'D LIKE.
WHAT ARE YOU GOING TO DO?
TRY SOME BIRD CALLS.
WATTERSON

Calvin and HOBBES
by WATTERSON
HA HA! RIGHT HERE, KID!
EEP!
HELP! HELP! THE LEAF PILE'S GOT ME!!
CRUNCH CRUNCH
WATTERSON
THE RAKE! GOTTA GET THE RAKE!
FORGET IT, KID! YOU'RE DOOMED!
YAAHH! BACK, YOU ARBOREAL MENACE! BACK!
WHAM WHAM
SINISTER FIEND! YOU WON'T BE TRICKING OTHER INNOCENT LITTLE KIDS! I'LL SPREAD YOU ACROSS THE WHOLE YARD!
I THOUGHT YOU SAID YOU WERE GOING TO RAKE THE YARD TODAY.
I DID RAKE THE YARD. I SPENT ALL AFTERNOO--
WHERE'S CALVIN?!

YOUR DAD AND I ARE GOING OUT TO SEE A MOVIE TONIGHT.
CAN I COME TOO?
NO, YOU'RE STAYING HOME.
WHAT, I GOT THE PLAGUE?! WHY CAN'T I COME?
BECAUSE OTHER PEOPLE LIKE TO WATCH MOVIES WITHOUT HEARING ADVICE SHOUTED TO THE CHARACTERS ON THE SCREEN.
SO WHO DOES **THAT**? ARE YOU SAYING **I** DO THAT?
WATTERSON

MOM WON'T LET US GO TO THE MOVIE WITH THEM, SO I GUESS WE'RE ON OUR OWN TONIGHT.
CAN WE WATCH TV?
WHAT MOM AND DAD DON'T KNOW WON'T HURT 'EM, RIGHT?
IN FACT, AFTER THEY LEAVE, LET'S GET IN THE OTHER CAR AND LEARN TO DRIVE!
OH BOY! I GET TO BEEP THE HORN, OK?
HEY, THERE'S A TEEN-AGER COMING UP THE DRIVE. OH NO! IT'S **ROSALYN**!
OUR BABY SITTER?! WHAT'S SHE DOING HERE? DON'T MOM AND DAD **TRUST** US?? QUICK, HIDE!!
WATTERSON

WE'RE LEAVING NOW, ROSALYN. CALVIN IS UPSTAIRS.
I HOPE HE'S NOT TOO MUCH TROUBLE TONIGHT.
DON'T WORRY, I BROUGHT A CATTLE PROD THIS TIME!
YOUR MOM AND DAD LAUGHED. MAYBE IT WAS A JOKE.
MAYBE MOM AND DAD THINK SCORCHING LITTLE KIDS IS FUNNY. LET'S GO.
WATTERSON

CALVIN? ARE YOU IN THERE? C'MON OUT AND WE'LL MAKE SOME POPCORN.
CALVIN? ...OH BROTHER...
I SEE YOU, CALVIN! C'MON BACK INSIDE!
NO WAY, LADY! IF YOU WANT US, YOU'LL HAVE TO CATCH US!
OUTTA MY WAY! OUTTA MY WAY!
OH GEEZ, RUN!! SHE'S WEARING CLEATS!

LET'S GO! BACK IN THE HOUSE! NO MORE MONKEY BUSINESS, ALL RIGHT?
PHOOEY.
IT'S MY JOB TO WATCH YOU AND THAT'S WHAT I'M GOING TO DO, EVEN IF I HAVE TO STRAP YOU TO A CHAIR.
GOT IT?
JAWOHL, MEIN FÜHRER!
CLIK
CARE TO REPEAT THAT LITTLE COMMENT?
I SAID I'M NOT GOING ANYWHERE. LEGGO.

WE'RE HOME, ROSALYN. WAS CALVIN ANY TROUBLE?
NOT TOO MUCH. I SENT HIM TO BED A LITTLE WHILE AGO.
THAT'S GOOD.
KNOCK KNOCK
NOW WHO COULD THAT BE AT THIS HOUR?
POLICE, SIR. WE RECEIVED A CALL ABOUT TWO HOSTAGES BEING HELD HERE.
CALVIN! GET DOWN HERE!!

Calvin and HOBBES
by WATTERSON
POW!
PANT WHEEZE
GASP
WELL, IF YOU DIDN'T GET IN A FIGHT AT SCHOOL, WHAT ON EARTH HAPPENED TO YOU ?!
LET'S JUST SAY SOMETIMES I WISH I HAD A GERBIL.
WATTERSON

UH OH, IT HAPPENED AGAIN.
CALVIN WAKES UP WITHOUT ANY RECOGNIZABLE FEATURES, SAVE TWO ANTENNAE. HOW DISGUSTING.
HE OOZES OUT OF BED ON A TRAIL OF SLIME. LACKING ARMS AND LEGS, HOW WILL CALVIN PUT ON HIS CLOTHES?
AREN'T YOU DRESSED YET? YOU ARE SO SLUGGISH IN THE MORNING!

PSST...SUSIE! WHAT'S THE ANSWER TO QUESTION FOUR?
IMADOOFUS.
THANKS!
THE TOOTH FAIRY'S GONNA MAKE YOU RICH TONIGHT, SUSIE.

LET'S SEE WHAT YOU DREW FOR ART CLASS, SUSIE.
WELL, A TIDY LITTLE DOMESTIC SCENE. A HOUSE IN A YARD WITH FLOWERS. HOW TYPICALLY FEMALE.
GIRLS THINK SMALL AND ARE PREOCCUPIED WITH PETTY DETAILS. BUT BOYS THINK BIG! BOYS THINK ABOUT ACTION AND ACCOMPLISHMENT! NO WONDER IT'S MEN WHO CHANGE THE WORLD!
YEAH? WHAT DID YOU DRAW?
A SQUADRON OF B-1s NUKING NEW YORK.

MOM, CAN HOBBES AND I RENT A VCR AND A TAPE TONIGHT?
I DON'T THINK SO, CALVIN. IT'S A SCHOOL NIGHT.
WHAT IF WE GOT AN EDUCATIONAL TAPE?
LIKE WHAT?
"CANNIBAL STEWARDESS VIXENS UNCHAINED."
NOW SHE WON'T EVEN LET US GO INTO THE STORE.
I THINK WE'D LEARN A LOT BY WATCHING THAT.

NOBODY HAD BETTER BE SNEAKING UP ON ME!!
WHUMP!
IT'S HARD TO CHANGE DIRECTION IN MID-AIR.
BUDDY, I'M GOING TO CHANGE A LOT MORE THAN YOUR DIRECTION.

SNIP SNAP CRACK
SHICKA SHICKA
WWHISSSSHHH
SHOOF SHOOF SHOOF SHOOF
KRITCH KRUNCH KRITCH KRUNCH
SOMETIMES IT'S GOOD TO HUSH UP A WHILE AND LET AUTUMN STICK IN A FEW WORDS.

Calvin and Hobbes
by WATTERSON
A DAZED SPACEMAN SPIFF CRAWLS FROM THE SMOKING WRECKAGE OF HIS SHIP!
OUR HERO NOW REGRETS NOT BUYING A TOWING RIDER ON HIS INSURANCE POLICY.
THE COURAGEOUS SPACEMAN SPIFF HAS BEEN CAPTURED BY THE HIDEOUS ZORGS OF PLANET X-13!
LED THROUGH THE DANK CORRIDORS OF THE DUNGEON, SPIFF LOOKS IN VAIN FOR AN OPPORTUNITY TO ESCAPE!
OUR HERO IS BROUGHT BEFORE THE ZORG DESPOT!
SO THIS IS THE FAMED SPACE EXPLORER SPIFF! I'VE WAITED A LONG TIME FOR THIS MOMENT, EARTHLING SCUM!
YOU HAVE KNOWLEDGE WE NEED. COOPERATE, AND WE'LL KILL YOU RATHER PAINLESSLY.
LET'S DISPENSE WITH THE PLEASANTRIES, YOU TWISTED SPACE CRUSTACEAN. WHAT IS IT YOU WANT FROM ME?
A SUMMARY OF LEWIS AND CLARK'S EXPEDITION TO THE PACIFIC!
HA! WILD ZONTARS COULDN'T DRAG THAT INFORMATION OUT OF ME! DO YOUR WORST!
YOU DIDN'T READ THE ASSIGNMENT, DID YOU, CALVIN?
WATTERSON

Hey, Calvin, c'mere.
SHOVE
Ha ha ha! What a weenie! Ha ha ha!
PEOPLE WHO GET NOSTALGIC ABOUT CHILDHOOD WERE OBVIOUSLY NEVER CHILDREN.

YOU LOOK DOWN IN THE DUMPS.
I AM.
MOE KEEPS KNOCKING ME DOWN AT SCHOOL FOR NO REASON. HE'S MEAN JUST FOR KICKS.
I SURE AM GLAD YOU'RE AN ANIMAL. ANIMALS SOMETIMES MAKE A LOT MORE SENSE THAN PEOPLE DO.
...AND WE'RE CUTER, TOO.
RIGHT, HOBBES. GOOD POINT.

LOOK, HOBBES, I NEED YOU TO COME TO SCHOOL WITH ME AND SHOW MOE A LITTLE FANG, OK?
YOU DON'T NEED TO KILL HIM OR ANYTHING. JUST GIVE 'IM SOMETHING TO THINK ABOUT ON THE WAY TO SURGERY.
HE USUALLY COMES AFTER ME AT RECESS, SO WE'LL GET HIM THEN. HEY, YOU DON'T HAVE RABIES, DO YOU?
CERTAINLY NOT.
RATS. WELL, I SUPPOSE HE'D AT LEAST HAVE TO GET A TETANUS SHOT.

HEY, CALVIN, WHY'D YOU BRING YOUR STUFFED TIGER TO SCHOOL? IT'S NOT A SHOW AND TELL DAY.
I KNOW. HOBBES IS GOING TO GIVE MOE A LITTLE "TREAT" TODAY: A RIDE IN AN AMBULANCE HELICOPTER.
YEAH? HOW'S HE GOING TO DO **THAT**?
IF YOU HAVE AN AVERSION TO DESCRIPTIONS OF CARNAGE, YOU PROBABLY DON'T WANT TO KNOW.
TALKING WITH YOU IS SORT OF THE CONVERSATIONAL EQUIVALENT OF AN OUT-OF-BODY EXPERIENCE.
DON'T GET TOO CLOSE NOW. I WANT HOBBES TO STAY FRESH FOR THIS AFTERNOON.
WATTERSON

Look, Calvin's got a teddy bear. That's real sweet, Cal.
IT'S A TIGER, YOU BRAINLESS INVERTEBRATE.
Hey, maybe I'd like to play with your teddy!
GOOD IDEA, MOE. HOBBES PLAYS KINDA ROUGH, BUT HE'S **LOTS** OF FUN. C'MERE AND TAKE HIM.
Why? Is the teacher watching? This is a trick, right? I'm not touching your stupid teddy, see?
C'MON, I DARE YOU! WHAT'S THE MATTER? ARE YOU CHICKEN?
WATTERSON
HA HA! BOY, YOU SURE SCARED **HIM** OFF! YOU WERE GREAT!
COME BACK AND CALL ME A "BEAR" AGAIN! YEAH, **YOU**, BUB!!

I CALLED YOUR TEACHER ABOUT MOE'S BULLYING, AND SHE SAID SHE'D PUT A STOP TO IT.
I'M AFRAID YOU WASTED YOUR TIME, MOM. MOE TOOK ONE LOOK AT HOBBES AND JUST ABOUT LOST HIS LUNCH!
I DON'T THINK MOE WILL BE BOTHERING **ME** FOR A WHILE. IT'S NOT EVERY KID WHO HAS A **TIGER** FOR A BEST FRIEND.
...AND WHAT LUCKY MOMS THOSE OTHER KIDS HAVE.
C'MON, HOBBES, IF YOU'LL LEND ME A BUCK, I'LL BUY YOU A COMIC BOOK.
WATTERSON

Calvin and Hobbes
by WATTERSON
I WISH IT WAS SATURDAY INSTEAD OF SUNDAY.
ANY DAY YOU HAVE TO TAKE A BATH AND GO TO BED EARLY ISN'T A DAY OFF IN MY BOOK.
AUTUMN SUNDAYS ARE THE WORST.
YOU CAN NEVER REALLY ENJOY SUNDAYS BECAUSE IN THE BACK OF YOUR MIND YOU KNOW YOU HAVE TO GO TO SCHOOL THE NEXT DAY.
AND WHEN THE LEAVES CHANGE COLOR IT JUST REMINDS YOU EVEN MORE THAT SUMMER'S OVER AND SCHOOL'S JUST BEGUN.
GEE, I LIKE THIS SEASON BEST OF ALL! THE TREES ARE LIKE NATURE'S OWN FIREWORKS DISPLAY!
I LOVE THE BRISK AIR, THE EARLY EVENINGS, THE... UH... THE... YES, WELL... HMM...
KAPOW! FWOOSH! ZINGG!
YOU DIDN'T MENTION FRESH APPLESAUCE, FUZZHEAD. DO YOU LIKE APPLESAUCE ?!?

PROCESSED LUNCH MEAT IS PRETTY SCARY. WHAT **ARE** THESE LITTLE SPECKS, ANYWAY? LIZARD PARTS? WHO KNOWS?
AND THIS "SKIN." I HEARD IT USED TO BE MADE OF INTESTINE, BUT I THINK NOWADAYS IT'S PLASTIC.
OF COURSE, THEY DYE AND WAX FRUIT SO IT LOOKS BETTER. IT'S LIKE EATING A CANDLE.
AND MOM WONDERS WHY I'M SO HUNGRY AFTER SCHOOL.
YEP, WE'D PROBABLY BE DEAD NOW IF IT WASN'T FOR TWINKIES.
WATTERSON

HEY, DAD, YOUR LATEST POLL JUST CAME IN. LET'S SEE WHAT IT SAYS.
BE STILL, MY HEART.
WELL, I'LL BE! YOUR POPULARITY IS IMPROVING! YOU WENT UP 30 POINTS!
REALLY?
HECK, NO WONDER! I'M READING THE GRAPH UPSIDE-DOWN. WHAT A KLUTZ I AM!
...HOPE YOU'RE ALL PACKED, DAD.
DON'T YOU HAVE SOME HOMEWORK TO DO?
WATTERSON

Z
Z
Z
SNIFF SNIFF
I LIKE TO MESS WITH HIS DREAMS.
ZZ...COOKIES? FOR ME? WHY SURE, BACK UP THE TRUCK... ZZZZ
WATTERSON

BU-URRP!
GOOD HEAVENS, CALVIN! WHAT DO WE SAY AFTER THAT?
"MUST BE A BARGE COMING THROUGH!"
WHAT DO YOU SAY?!
"THAT SURE TASTED BETTER GOING DOWN THAN COMING UP!"
THREE STRIKES AND YOU'RE HISTORY, KIDDO.
EXCUSE ME.

WITH ULTRA-SONIC HEARING, STUPENDOUS MAN NOTICES A CRY OF DISTRESS FROM A DISTANT ALLEYWAY!
HE LEAPS TO THE EDGE OF THE BUILDING AND PREPARES TO SWOOP TO THE RESCUE!
STUPENDOUS MAN HAD NOT QUITE REALIZED JUST HOW HIGH UP HE WAS, HOWEVER. AT THIS ALTITUDE THE WINDS WERE A LITTLE TRICKY, AND...
ARE YOU GOING, OR DO YOU NEED A PUSH?
DON'T RUSH ME, ALL RIGHT?!

ACK! ICK!
ACKPT! GHK!
HA-HA HA HA
BLECHTH GAKCK
LURCH YOUR WAY TO THE CAR, KID. YOU NEED A HAIRCUT.

Calvin and HOBBES
by WATTERSON
YOUR DAD'S WORKING, SO TRY NOT TO BOTHER HIM, OK?
DAD, I HAVE A QUESTION.
YES?
DO PEOPLE EVER SPONTANEOUSLY COMBUST?
UH... NOT THAT I KNOW OF, NO.
THAT'S A RELIEF. THANKS, DAD.
YOU'RE WELCOME.
POW!
DID I FOOL YOU?
IF YOU'RE HAVING TROUBLE THINKING OF WAYS TO MAKE YOURSELF USEFUL, I'LL GIVE YOU SOME SUGGESTIONS.

THINK IT'S GETTING ANY COLDER OUT?
NOT REALLY.
I DON'T THINK IT'S GONNA CHANGE.
ME EITHER.
NUTS. WELL, LET'S GO IN.
WATTERSON

WHATCHA DOIN'?
COUNTERFEITING MONEY.
IT'S REALLY HARD. LOOK AT ALL THE LITTLE LINES ON THIS BILL.
THINK ANYONE WILL FALL FOR YOUR FORGERY?
SURE. EVERYONE WILL.
WATTERSON
OL' GEORGE HAS THE GOUT, I SEE.
I **SAID** THIS WAS HARD.

THE GIANT WHALE SWIMS TOWARD THE SURFACE!
ITS MASSIVE TAIL PUMPING FURIOUSLY, HE GAINS TERRIFYING MOMENTUM!
THE 35-TON BEHEMOTH BREACHES! HE CRASHES INTO THE SURF WITH DEAFENING IMPACT!
CALVIN, YOU'D BETTER NOT BE SPLASHING THE FLOOR, YOU HEAR ME?!
WATTERSON

STIR
STIR
STIR
STIR
STIR
STIR
I WON'T EAT ANY CEREAL THAT DOESN'T TURN THE MILK PURPLE.
MILK

THE DEADLY TORNADO MAKES ITS WAY ACROSS THE COMMUNITY!
THE CIRCLING UPDRAFT CLOCKS AT OVER 200 MPH! THE TWISTER SEARCHES FOR A TRAILER PARK!
FINDING ONE, IT TOUCHES DOWN! DEBRIS IS THROWN FOR MILES IN THE ENSUING EXPLOSION OF RUSHING AIR!
WHEN ARE YOU GOING TO CLEAN UP THIS ROOM?! IT LOOKS LIKE A...
TORNADO HIT IT, I KNOW.

OH BOY, IT'S SATURDAY!!
WHAT'S GOING ON? WHY AREN'T THERE ANY CARTOONS ON TV? IT'S JUST A TEST PATTERN.
THE TV GUIDE SAYS THEY DON'T START UNTIL 6:30.
HECK, THAT'S 45 MINUTES FROM NOW! WELL, C'MON, I'LL RACE YOU UP AND DOWN THE STAIRS!
WHY CAN'T HE EVER GET UP LIKE THIS ON SCHOOL DAYS?
GO BREAK HIS LITTLE LEGS, WILL YOU, HONEY?
BANG!
BONK

Calvin and Hobbes
by WATTERSON
KISS HOBBES GOOD NIGHT TOO, MOM.
IF YOU DON'T GET A GOOD NIGHT KISS, YOU GET KAFKA DREAMS.
SLEEP TIGHT. "DON'T LET THE BEDBUGS BITE."
WHAT'S THAT SUPPOSED TO MEAN? DO WE HAVE VERMIN IN THIS HOUSE?!?
THE MATTRESS IS MOVING!
WHOA! IT MUST BE A BEDBUG!
GAAH! LEGS!! IT MUST BE HUGE! HOW DISGUSTING! UGGHH!!
I'LL RUN FOR SOME BUG SPRAY! DON'T LET HIM OUT!
I NEED MORE WEIGHT! PUT YOUR FOOT LOCKER UP HERE!
WHAT'S GOING ON UP THERE?!
IT SOUNDS LIKE HE'S MOVING FURNITURE!
I GOT SOME RAID! LIFT UP THE MATTRESS!
LET HIM HAVE IT!
GOSH, ALL THAT SPRAY DIDN'T KILL HIM! WHAT ARE WE GONNA DO?!
I HEAR YOUR DAD COMING! MAYBE HE CAN KILL IT!
WATTERSON
ABOUT TIME, DAD! HE CRAWLED BACK INTO THE BED! GET A FLY SWATTER!
I'LL (COUGH) TELL YOU WHO'S GOING TO GET SWATTED! (CHOKE) WHAT HAVE YOU DONE TO THIS ROOM?!!

BAD NEWS ON YOUR CAMPAIGN TO STAY DAD, DAD.
OH?
YEP. THE LATEST POLL OF SIX-YEAR-OLDS IN THIS HOUSEHOLD SHOWS THAT THEY DON'T CARE ABOUT ISSUES THIS YEAR. IT'S CHARACTER THAT COUNTS.
SO WHY IS THAT BAD NEWS?
WHO'S THE BIMBO WITH YOU IN THIS OLD PROM PICTURE?
THAT "BIMBO" IS YOUR MOTHER!
WHO'S A BIMBO?!
PRETTY FUNKY HAIRDO, MOM!

IT'S THE SAD TRUTH, DAD. NOBODY CARES ABOUT YOUR POSITIONS ON FATHERHOOD. WE JUST WANT TO KNOW ABOUT YOUR CHARACTER.
IF YOU'RE GOING TO BE DAD HERE, WE HAVE TO KNOW YOU'VE NEVER DONE OR SAID ANYTHING THAT WOULD REFLECT POORLY ON YOUR JUDGMENT.
I HAVE YOUR COLLEGE YEARBOOK HERE. LET'S FLIP THROUGH IT, SHALL WE?
IS THIS YOU WITH THE KEG AND THE "PARTY NAKED" T-SHIRT?
GIVE ME THAAAT!

GRANDPA SAYS THE COMICS WERE A LOT BETTER YEARS AGO WHEN NEWSPAPERS PRINTED THEM BIGGER.
HE SAYS COMICS NOW ARE JUST A BUNCH OF XEROXED TALKING HEADS BECAUSE THERE'S NO SPACE TO TELL A DECENT STORY OR TO SHOW ANY ACTION.
HE THINKS PEOPLE SHOULD WRITE TO THEIR NEWSPAPERS AND COMPLAIN.
YOUR GRANDPA TAKES THE FUNNIES PRETTY SERIOUSLY.
YEAH, MOM'S LOOKING INTO NURSING HOMES.

DID YOU READ THIS? THIS TV STAR MADE OVER TWENTY MILLION DOLLARS LAST YEAR!
WHAT WOULD ***YOU*** DO WITH TWENTY MILLION BUCKS?
BEATS ME. I THINK IT'S RIDICULOUS THAT ANYONE MAKES THAT KIND OF MONEY.
OK, SAY YOU ONLY MADE ***FIFTEEN*** MILLION.
LET'S SAY EIGHTEEN.
WATTERSON

HI, MOM.
BUM BA DA BUM BUM
WHAT'S COOKING?
HA HA HA HA HA HA!
WHAT'S WITH ***YOU***?
I THOUGHT MY LIFE WOULD SEEM MORE INTERESTING WITH A MUSICAL SCORE AND A LAUGH TRACK.
WATTERSON

I MADE UP A JOKE. A MAN'S GOING FOR A WALK, SO HE GETS HIS DOG AND SAYS, "HEEL!"
..AND THE DOG LOOKS UP AND SAYS, "IT TAKES ONE TO KNOW ONE, BUSTER!" HA HA HA HA HA!!
WATTERSON
WHAT'S THE MATTER WITH YOU? DON'T YOU ***GET*** IT?!
AHHH, WHAT DO TIGERS KNOW ABOUT SOPHISTICATED HUMOR, ANYWAY?
HOW DID THE DOG LEARN TO TALK?

Calvin and HOBBES
GO WAY BACK. I'M REALLY GONNA BELT THIS.
by WATTERSON
KEEP GOING. KEEP GOING.
I SAID WAY BACK! KEEP GOING!
THAT DUMMY. HE CAN'T KICK IT THIS FAR.
BOOT
WHUMP
WHAT'RE YA DOIN'? I'M TEN YARDS FROM THE GOAL LINE! AREN'T YOU GONNA TRY TO CATCH ME ?!?
I COULD CRAWL ON MY HANDS AND KNEES TO MAKE A TOUCHDOWN BEFORE YOU'D EVER GET ME FROM BACK THERE! WHAT'S THE MATTER WITH YOU?!?
OOPS.
POW!
DO YOU WANT TO KEEP TRYING FOR THE LAST TWO YARDS, OR JUST GIVE ME THE BALL NOW?
I CALL A TEN YEAR TIME OUT TO GROW SOME MORE.
WATTERSON

HI, SUSIE. WHAT DO YOU HAVE FOR LUNCH TODAY?
DON'T EVEN TALK TO ME. I DON'T WANT TO HEAR HOW DISGUSTING YOU THINK MY LUNCH IS. MY LUNCH IS FINE.
RELAX. I WASN'T GOING TO SAY A WORD ABOUT YOUR LUNCH. PASS ME SOME SALT, WILL YOU PLEASE?
HERE.
THANKS. SLUGS ARE SO CHEWY BEFORE YOU SHRIVEL 'EM UP.

I'M HOME!
BOINGG
POW!
I READ THAT TIGERS' SPINAL COLUMNS ARE LIKE BIG COILED SPRINGS!
I READ THAT THEIR BRAINS ARE LIKE BIG BOWLS OF TAPIOCA.

BLECCHH! HOW LONG ARE THOSE TWO GONNA KEEP KISSING? THIS PROGRAM ONLY LASTS AN HOUR!
GEEZ, LOOK AT THEM SLOBBERING OVER EACH OTHER'S FACES! WHY WOULD ANYBODY DO THAT? DO THEY LIKE IT?
BED TIME.
THERE'S A CONNECTION HERE, I JUST KNOW IT.

QUIT HOGGING THE BED. YOU'RE WAY OVER ON MY SIDE.
TOUGH BEANS, FUZZ FACE.
EVER THINK ABOUT GEYSERS AND WATERFALLS? HUNDREDS OF THOUSANDS OF GALLONS OF WATER! FLOWING, SPILLING, RUSHING, GUSHING, SPLASHING!
HE REALLY FIGHTS MEAN.

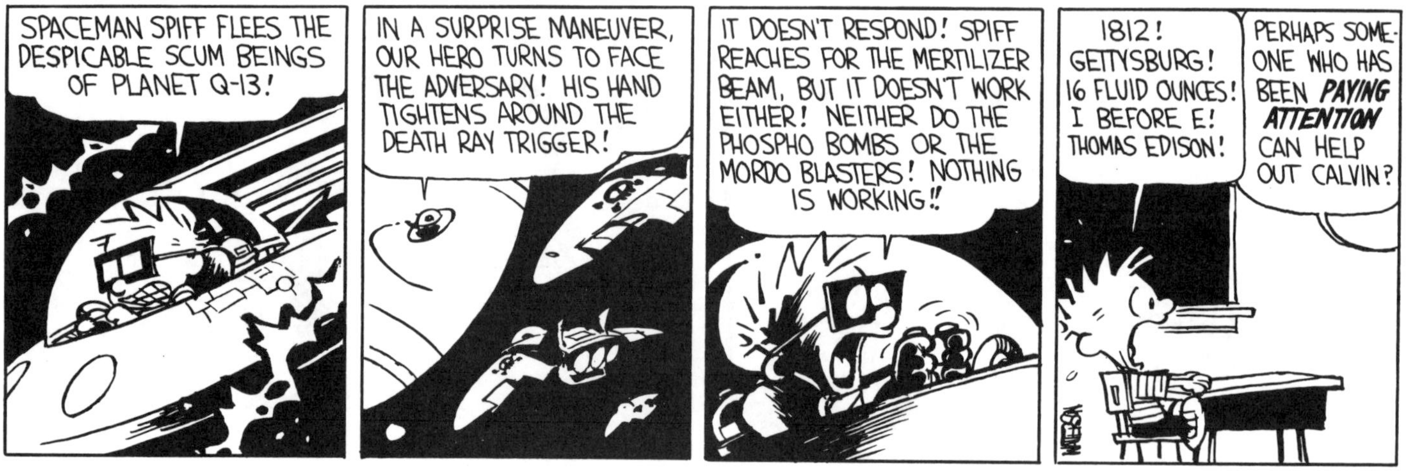
SPACEMAN SPIFF FLEES THE DESPICABLE SCUM BEINGS OF PLANET Q-13!
IN A SURPRISE MANEUVER, OUR HERO TURNS TO FACE THE ADVERSARY! HIS HAND TIGHTENS AROUND THE DEATH RAY TRIGGER!
IT DOESN'T RESPOND! SPIFF REACHES FOR THE MERTILIZER BEAM, BUT IT DOESN'T WORK EITHER! NEITHER DO THE PHOSPHO BOMBS OR THE MORDO BLASTERS! NOTHING IS WORKING!!
1812! GETTYSBURG! 16 FLUID OUNCES! I BEFORE E! THOMAS EDISON!
PERHAPS SOMEONE WHO HAS BEEN ***PAYING ATTENTION*** CAN HELP OUT CALVIN?

Z
YAAHH!
I KEEP FORGETTING THAT FIVE OF HIS SIX ENDS ARE POINTY WHEN HE LIES LIKE THAT.

Calvin and HOBBES
by WATTERSON
IF YOU DON'T HURRY UP, YOU'LL MISS THE SCHOOL BUS.
THAT'S THE BEST NEWS I'VE HEARD TODAY.
LET'S SEE, WHAT SHOULD I WEAR TODAY?
AAUGH!
NOW, BOYS! GET 'IM!
HELP HELP HELP HELP HELP
HOLD HIS ARMS! GRAB HIS FEET!
WATTERSON
OK BOYS, JUST LIKE WE PLANNED! STRIPED PANTS! POLKA DOT SHIRT! PLAID JACKET! EVERYBODY ON!
HEY!
I'M NOT GOING OUT LIKE THIS! GET OFF ME!
LIFT HIS LEGS! MAKE HIM WALK!
LOOK AT YOU! HAVE YOU GONE COLORBLIND??
I DON'T WANT TO HEAR ABOUT IT.

SINCE SEPTEMBER, IT'S JUST GOTTEN COLDER AND COLDER.
THERE'S LESS DAYLIGHT NOW, I'VE NOTICED, TOO.
OH NO! THIS CAN ONLY MEAN ONE THING!
THE SUN IS GOING OUT! IN A FEW MORE MONTHS EARTH WILL BE A DARK AND LIFELESS BALL OF ICE!
WELL, GEE, NOW I DON'T FEEL SO BAD ABOUT NOT SETTING UP AN IRA LAST YEAR.

DAD SAYS THE SUN ISN'T GOING OUT.
HE SAYS IT'S COLDER BECAUSE OUR HEMISPHERE IS TILTED AWAY FROM THE SUN NOW.
HE SAYS WINTER WILL BE HERE SOON.
ISN'T IT SAD HOW SOME PEOPLE'S GRIP ON THEIR LIVES IS SO PRECARIOUS THAT THEY'LL EMBRACE ANY PREPOSTEROUS DELUSION RATHER THAN FACE AN OCCASIONAL BLEAK TRUTH?

ARE YOU GOING TO LIVE THE LAST FEW MONTHS OF YOUR LIFE ANY DIFFERENTLY, NOW THAT THE SUN IS GOING OUT AND WE'RE ALL DOOMED?
NO, I'VE ALWAYS BELIEVED IN LIVING EACH DAY AS IF IT WAS MY LAST, SO I NEVER HAVE ANY REGRETS.
KIND OF INSPIRING, HUH?
IF YOU WERE SOMEONE ELSE, IT MIGHT BE.
PASS ME THAT ISSUE OF CAPTAIN NAPALM WILL YOU?
COOKIES

MY TEACHER SAID THE SAME THING DAD DID. THE SUN *ISN'T* GOING OUT AFTER ALL!
IT'S JUST GETTING COLDER BECAUSE WINTER'S COMING. DAD WAS RIGHT ALL ALONG!
IMAGINE OL' DAD KNOWING SOMETHING LIKE THAT!

WHAT'S THIS STORY YOU'RE GOING TO READ ME, DAD? IT DOESN'T HAVE ANY ROMANCE IN IT, DOES IT?
UH...
EDIT IT OUT IF IT DOES. I HATE ROMANCE. DOES IT HAVE ANY BORING DESCRIPTION IN IT?
WELL...
SKIP IT IF YOU SEE ANY. I LIKE MY STORIES FAST AND GRIPPING.
IT DOESN'T HAVE A MORAL, DOES IT? I HATE BEING TOLD HOW TO LIVE MY LIFE. SKIP THE MORAL, TOO, OK?
DOES HIS MAJESTY PREFER COLOR PICTURES, OR BLACK AND WHITE?

THE MIGHTY DESTROYER PATROLS THE SEAS!
SUDDENLY THE SHIP SPINS OUT OF CONTROL! IT'S CAUGHT IN A WHIRLPOOL!
WITHIN MOMENTS THE GIANT VESSEL DIPS ITS HULL INTO THE SWIRLING VORTEX AND IS NEVER SEEN AGAIN!
OH NO! HERE GOES THE REST OF THE NAVY!
ARE YOU LETTING THE WATER OUT *ALREADY?*

Calvin and HOBBES
by WATTERSON
ZZ-ZZZ
BBWAAAAHH
CALVIN, IT'S TIME TO WAKE UP.
Z
SUGAR BOMBS
CALVIN, IT'S TIME TO WAKE UP.
C'MON, YOU'LL BE LATE FOR SCHOOL.
Z
MY DREAMS ARE GETTING WAY TOO LITERAL.
WATTERSON

I'M GOING TO BE THE NEXT HOUDINI! TIE ME TO THIS CHAIR AND I'LL ESCAPE!
TIE THE KNOTS TIGHTER. DON'T MAKE IT SO EASY FOR ME. TIE MY FEET, TOO.
ALL RIGHT, LET'S SEE YOU GET OUT OF THAT.
HA! THE GREAT CALVINI CAN ESCAPE FROM ANYTHING!
CALVIN, DINNER TIME!
SHOULD I TELL HER YOU'RE TIED UP AT THE MOMENT, HA HA?
I'LL BE (MMF) OUT OF HERE (RRG) IN NO TIME. GOSH, I CAN'T EVEN MOVE.

YOUR DINNER'S GETTING COLD, CALVIN!
I'LL BE DOWN IN A SECOND.
YOU WANT ME TO HELP UNTIE YOU?
NO! DON'T TOUCH THOSE ROPES! I WANT TO ESCAPE!
IT'S EASY. I JUST ROCK A LITTLE TO LOOSEN THE KNOTS. NO ROPES CAN HOLD ME!
WHOOP!
OW!!
GOOD THING YOU'RE DOING THIS HERE BEFORE YOU TRIED IT UNDER WATER.

MMF! GGGK! IT'S NO USE. YOU'D BETTER UNTIE ME. I CAN'T ESCAPE.
LET'S SEE, THIS END GOES IN HERE, AND AROUND OVER THERE. YOU KNOW, KNOTS ARE PRETTY TRICKY.
HURRY UP.
IF I PULL ON THIS, IT SHOULD...
AAH! THAT'S TIGHTER! PULL THE OTHER WAY! THE OTHER WAY!
CALVIN, THIS IS THE LAST CHANCE FOR DINNER! GET DOWN HERE!
"SIT TIGHT," HA HA! I'LL GET YOUR CUB SCOUT MANUAL.
I DON'T BELIEVE THIS.

I ALWAYS WANTED TO BE A CUB SCOUT AND GET MERIT BADGES AND STUFF, BUT I HATE GOING TO MEETINGS.
OK OK, JUST READ ABOUT KNOTS, ALL RIGHT?
HEY, LOOK, HERE'S A MOTTO! I DIDN'T KNOW YOU HAD A MOTTO! WOW, WHAT FUN!
"LIVE FOR REVENGE" IS GOING TO BE MY MOTTO IF YOU DON'T GET ME OUT OF THIS.
I'LL QUIZ YOU. WHAT DO YOU DO FOR A SECOND-DEGREE BURN?
DON'T FLIP THROUGH THE BOOK, YOU IDIOT! UNTIE ME!
HMPH, IF *I* WAS IN **YOUR** PREDICAMENT, I'D TREAT ME WITH A LOT MORE RESPECT. DO YOU SAY YOU'RE SORRY?
MMFF! RRGGH! OOH! ARGH! YOU DIRTY ROTTEN STINKING

HOBBES, I'M NOT KIDDING. IF YOU DON'T GET ME LOOSE IN TEN SECONDS...
YOU GOT YOURSELF INTO THIS, "MR. HOUDINI," NOT ME.
BUT I'M SUPPOSED TO BE AT DINNER! MOM'S GONNA KILL ME!
ESCAPE ARTISTS HAVE A RISKY TRADE. HEY, HERE'S MORSE CODE!
OK, I'M SORRY I CALLED YOU NAMES. I SAID I'M SORRY, RIGHT? NOW UNTIE ME!
HERE'S HOW YOU SAY "BANANA" IN MORSE. DASH DOT DOT DOT, DOT DASH...
WHAT IS THAT KID ***DOING***?!
IT SOUNDS LIKE A CHAIR THUMPING AROUND THE ROOM.
BONK
BONK
WELL, HIS DINNER IS STONE COLD. I HOPE HE'S HAPPY.

ALL RIGHT, YOUNG MAN! YOU'VE WASTED THE NICE MEAL YOUR MOM FIXED. GET OUT HERE.
YOU TIED YOURSELF UP?? WHAT ON EARTH WERE YOU ***DOING***?!
HOBBES TIED ME UP, DAD! IT'S ***HIS*** FAULT!
DON'T MAKE UP LIES, CALVIN. HOW DID YOU GET YOURSELF LIKE THIS?!
HOBBES DID IT, DAD! HE WAS GOING TO HOLD ME FOR RANSOM! HONEST!
RANSOM?? WHO'D PAY FOR ***YOU***, YOU BIG FIBBER?! I'M CERTAINLY GLAD YOUR DAD SAW THROUGH ***THAT*** FILTHY LIE!
OH, HUSH. YOU ***ALWAYS*** GET ME IN TROUBLE.

Calvin and HOBBES by WATERSON
First there was nothing...
...then there was Calvin!
Calvin, the mighty god, creates the universe with pure will!
From utter nothingness comes swirling form! Life begins where once was void!
But Calvin is no kind and loving god! He's one of the old gods! He demands sacrifice!
Yes, Calvin is a god of the underworld! And the puny inhabitants of earth displease him!
The great Calvin ignores their pleas for mercy and the doomed writhe in agony!
HAVE YOU SEEN HOW ABSORBED CALVIN IS WITH THOSE TINKERTOYS? HE'S CREATING WHOLE WORLDS OVER THERE!
I'LL BET HE GROWS UP TO BE AN ARCHITECT.
WATERSON

WHAT'S FOR DINNER, MOM?
TORTELLINI.
OH, NO, NOT TORTELLINI! I HATE TORTELLINI!! OH, GROSS! YECCH! TORTELLINI!!
NOTHING IS MORE DISGUSTING THAN TORTELLINI!! CAN'T WE HAVE SOMETHING ELSE?
NO.
TORTELLINI... TORTELLINI... T-O-R...
DICTIONARY

DID YOU SEE WE HAVE A SUBSTITUTE TEACHER TODAY?
OH, NO! THAT CAN ONLY MEAN OUR REAL TEACHER ROCKETED BACK TO SATURN TO REPORT TO HER SUPERIORS!
THEY'RE TRYING TO SUBVERT US LITTLE KIDS WITH SUBLIMINAL MESSAGES IN OUR TEXTBOOKS, TELLING US TO TURN IN OUR PARENTS WHEN THE SATURNIANS ATTACK! EARTH WILL BE RENDERED HELPLESS!
I THINK ONE OF US HAS BEEN EATING TOO MUCH PASTE IN ART CLASS.
I'M TOO SMART FOR 'EM, THOUGH! I DON'T READ MY ASSIGNMENTS!

BEHOLD THE TERRIBLE THUNDER LIZARD, TYRANNOSAURUS REX!
THE FIERCEST DINOSAUR OF ALL, HE IS TWENTY TONS OF BONE-CRUSHING MUSCLE AND RAZOR-SHARP TEETH!
ALWAYS THE VICTOR, HE LETS OUT A TRIUMPHANT ROAR!
LIBRARY
BOOT

AH.. AH.. AH..
I JUTH *HADE* IT WHED THITH HAPPEDTH.

CALVIN THE CRIMINAL IS ABOUT TO FACE JUSTICE! ANGRY THRONGS TURN OUT TO WATCH HIS EXECUTION!
AS HE IS LED UP THE GALLOWS, HE REFLECTS UPON HIS MANY HEINOUS CRIMES. HE IS NOT REPENTANT!
THE NOOSE IS PUT AROUND HIS NECK AND TIGHTENED! THIS IS THE END!
GACKK URRGHH
OH, KNOCK IT OFF. SOME OF US HAVE TO WEAR A TIE EVERY DAY.

HOW WAS THE KIDDY MATINEE MOVIE?
MOVIE? OH, YEAH, THE MOVIE. YEAH, THERE WAS A MOVIE. IT WAS OK, I GUESS.
HOW WAS THE MATINEE?
WE... ARE... BUYING... A VIDEO PLAYER.

CALVIN and HOBBES
by WATTERSON
YAWN
PUTT PUTT PUTT PUTT PUTT PUTT
Z
SCRITCH SCRATCH
ZZ
MMM..
RUB RUB RUB
ZZ
..RRRR..
SHOOF SHOOF SHOOF
ZZ
.OOO..MM..
ITCH ITCH ITCH ITCH
ZZ
YOW WOW
YOW WOW
ZZ..
NKG
K
ZZ..
HMMMMM
ZZZ
Z
THAT SIGH OUGHT TO GET ME OUT OF A FEW YEARS' PURGATORY.
Z
WATTERSON

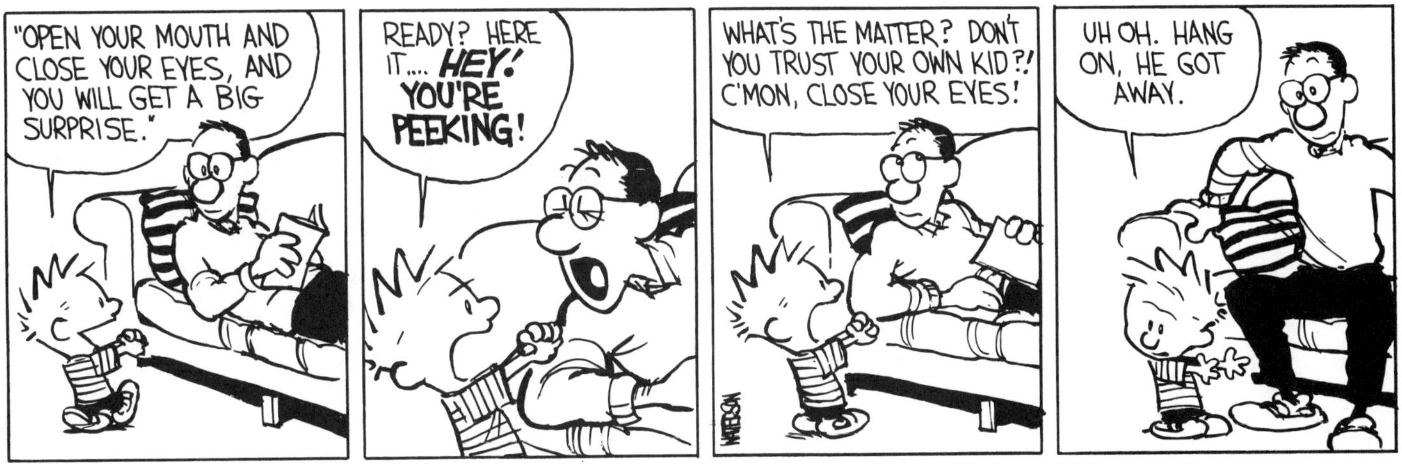
"OPEN YOUR MOUTH AND CLOSE YOUR EYES, AND YOU WILL GET A BIG SURPRISE."
READY? HERE IT.... HEY! YOU'RE PEEKING!
WHAT'S THE MATTER? DON'T YOU TRUST YOUR OWN KID?! C'MON, CLOSE YOUR EYES!
UH OH. HANG ON, HE GOT AWAY.

ANYTHING YET?
NOT ONE SNOW-FLAKE.

BATH TIME, CALVIN!
COME ON, LET'S JUST GET IT OVER WITH THIS TIME, ALL RIGHT?
WHERE ARE YOU? LET'S GO!
SHE'LL NEVER LOOK HERE.

Calvin and Hobbes
by WATTERSON
I DON'T KNOW, CALVIN. IT'S AWFULLY EXPENSIVE.
CAN WE GET THIS TREE, MOM? CAN WE?
YEAH, BUT JUST THINK HOW MUCH LOOT WOULD FIT UNDER IT!
DAD! COME BRING IN THE CHRISTMAS TREE MOM AND I PICKED! IT'S A GREAT ONE!
THIS YEAR I THOUGHT WE'D JUST KEEP THE TREE IN THE GARAGE.
IN THE GARAGE?!
SURE. YOU CAN GO OUT AND LOOK AT IT ANY TIME YOU LIKE, AND IT SAVES ALL THE TROUBLE OF DECORATING IT.
WE'RE NOT GOING TO DECORATE IT?!?
WHY BOTHER? WE JUST TAKE IT ALL DOWN IN TWO WEEKS. ON CHRISTMAS DAY, IF YOU GET A PRESENT...
WATTERSON
IF I GET A PRESENT?!
...YOU CAN TAKE IT OUT TO THE GARAGE TO OPEN, AND PRETEND THE TREE HAS LOTS OF LIGHTS, AND...
MOMMMM!
I KNOW SOMEBODY WHO'S GOING TO GET A LOT OF COAL IN HIS STOCKING, BUSTER.
THIS SEASON GETS LESS JOLLY EVERY YEAR.

Dear Santa,
Attached is my Christmas list for this year.
Last year I did not receive several items from my List.
For your convenience, I have grouped those items together on page 12. Please check them carefully, and include them with the rest of my loot this year.
THAT'S THE PROBLEM WITH THIS GUY. HE'S GOTTEN SLOPPY WITHOUT ANY COMPETITION.
WATTERSON

HE SEES YOU WHEN YOU'RE SLEEPING, HE KNOWS WHEN YOU'RE AWAKE ...
HE KNOWS IF YOU'VE BEEN BAD OR GOOD, SO BE GOOD FOR GOODNESS SAKE!
* CLICK *
SANTA CLAUS: KINDLY OLD ELF, OR CIA SPOOK?
WATTERSON

THIS SANTA CLAUS STUFF BOTHERS ME.... ESPECIALLY THE JUDGE AND JURY BIT.
WHO APPOINTED SANTA? HOW DO WE KNOW HE'S IMPARTIAL? WHAT CRITERIA DOES HE USE FOR DETERMINING GOOD AND BAD?
AND WHAT ABOUT EXTENUATING CIRCUMSTANCES? KIDS SHOULD HAVE THE BENEFIT OF LEGAL COUNSEL, DON'T YOU THINK?
YOU'RE WORRIED ABOUT THE SALAMANDER INCIDENT, AREN'T YOU?
TEMPORARY INSANITY! THAT'S ALL IT WAS!
WATTERSON

THEY SAY SANTA KNOWS IF YOU'VE BEEN GOOD OR BAD, BUT WHAT IF SOMEONE HAD BEEN SORT OF **BOTH**?
I MEAN, SUPPOSE SOME KID ***TRIED*** TO BE GOOD...AT LEAST, WELL, MOST OF THE TIME...BUT BAD THINGS INEXPLICABLY KEPT HAPPENING?
SUPPOSE SOME KID JUST HAD TERRIBLE LUCK, AND HE GOT BLAMED FOR A LOT OF THINGS HE DID ONLY ***SORT*** OF ON PURPOSE?
WHO EXACTLY MIGHT WE BE TALKING ABOUT?
THIS IS A PURELY HYPOTHETICAL CASE, MR. SMARTYPANTS.

THIS WHOLE SANTA CLAUS THING JUST DOESN'T MAKE SENSE.
WHY ALL THE SECRECY? WHY ALL THE MYSTERY? IF THE GUY EXISTS, WHY DOESN'T HE EVER SHOW HIMSELF AND PROVE IT?
AND IF HE ***DOESN'T*** EXIST, WHAT'S THE MEANING OF ALL THIS?
I DUNNO... ISN'T THIS A RELIGIOUS HOLIDAY?
YEAH, BUT ACTUALLY, I'VE GOT THE SAME QUESTIONS ABOUT GOD.

GOSH, HOBBES, WHAT IF I DON'T GET ANY PRESENTS THIS YEAR BECAUSE I DOUBTED THE EXISTENCE OF SANTA?
SUPPOSE HE'S PUTTING MY NAME ON THE "BAD" LIST RIGHT NOW! THAT WOULD BE AWFUL!
PERSONALLY, I'D THINK THAT IF YOU WEREN'T ON THE "BAD" LIST ALL ALONG, THIS WOULDN'T PUSH YOU OVER.
THANKS FOR THE COMFORT, EGGNOG BRAIN.
SEE? ***SEE*** WHY YOU'RE ON THE "BAD" LIST? INSULTS!

WELL, I'VE DECIDED I **DO** BELIEVE IN SANTA CLAUS, NO MATTER HOW PREPOSTEROUS HE SOUNDS.
WHAT CONVINCED YOU?
A SIMPLE RISK ANALYSIS.
I WANT PRESENTS. **LOTS** OF PRESENTS. WHY RISK NOT GETTING THEM OVER A MATTER OF BELIEF? HECK, I'LL BELIEVE ANYTHING THEY WANT.
HOW CYNICALLY ENTERPRISING OF YOU.
IT'S THE SPIRIT OF CHRISTMAS.

PSST! ARE YOU AWAKE?
OF COURSE.
I HAVEN'T HEARD SANTA YET, HAVE YOU? DO YOU THINK HE'S COMING?
IT'S ONLY 11:00. WE MAY BE LATER ON THE ROUTE.
THUMP!
GASP DID YOU HEAR THAT?
IT'S HIM! IT'S SANTA! SHHH! HE'S SAYING SOMETHING!
SLIPPIN' RIPPIN' DANG FANG ROTTEN ZARG BARG-A-DING DONG!
QUIET, DEAR! CALVIN WILL HEAR YOU!

WE GOT PRESENTS! SANTA CAME! HE CAME! HE CAME!
OH, NO... IT'S NOT MORNING ALREADY?
WELL, TECHNICALLY, YES...

Calvin and Hobbes
by WATTERSON
HERE'S A BOX OF CRAYONS. I NEED SOME ILLUSTRATIONS FOR A STORY I'M WRITING.
YOU CAN DRAW SOMETHING BESIDES TIGERS, CAN'T YOU?
SURE. LEOPARDS, PUMAS, OCELOTS.. ..YOU NAME IT.
HERE, DAD, READ THIS STORY TONIGHT. I WROTE IT AND HOBBES ILLUSTRATED IT.
..UM... OK.
"THE DAD WHO LIVED TO REGRET BEING MEAN TO HIS KID."
WHAT ARE YOU PAUSING FOR? KEEP READING.
Barney's dad was really bad, So Barney hatched a plan. When his dad said, "Eat your peas!" Barney shouted, "NO!" and ran.
peas
Barney
Barney tricked his mean ol' dad, And locked him in the cellar. His mom never found out where he'd gone, 'Cause Barney didn't tell her.
door
key
There his dad spent his life, Eating mice and gruel. With every bite for fifty years He was sorry he'd been cruel. THE END.
Barney's dad
mice
YOU KNOW HOW A LOT OF STORIES HAVE MORALS TO THEM...?
I GET IT, I GET IT!
WATTERSON & HOBS

WHAT DO YOU THINK IS THE MEANING OF TRUE HAPPINESS?
IS IT MONEY, CARS AND WOMEN?
...OR IS IT JUST MONEY AND CARS?
WELL-L-L-L?

LOOK AT THIS! YOU CALL THIS SNOW?!
IT'S NOT EVEN AN INCH HIGH! WHAT GOOD IS LESS THAN AN INCH OF SNOW?!
WELL, IT'S PRETTY.
NOBODY EVER CLOSED A SCHOOL ON ACCOUNT OF PRETTINESS.

THIS WILL BE THE STRONGEST SNOW FORT EVER MADE!
KEEP PACKING ON SNOW. THIS WILL BE INDESTRUCTIBLE.
WE'LL POUR WATER ON IT, SO IT FREEZES OVERNIGHT. THAT WAY OUR FORT WILL BE HERE UNTIL JULY!
WHERE'S THAT KID?!

THIS SNOW FORT CAN REPEL ANY ATTACK!
I HATE THIS NEIGHBORHOOD.
WATTERSON

WHAP!
?
?
?
?
WATTERSON
I'M GLAD TO SEE *YOU'RE* INSIDE.
IT'S HANDY NOT TO HAVE BOOTS AND A COAT TO TAKE OFF.

MY SNOW FORT MAKES ME INVULNERABLE!
FROM BEHIND ITS THICK WALL, I CAN LAUNCH A BRUTAL SNOWBALL BARRAGE AND REMAIN SAFE FROM RETALIATION!
WHAP!
YOU'RE SUPPOSED TO ATTACK FROM *THAT* SIDE OF THE FORT, DUMMY!!
WATTERSON

Calvin and HOBBES
by WATTERSON
HOP HOP HOP HOP
HOP HOP
DID YOU MAKE ANY RESOLUTIONS FOR THE NEW YEAR?
HECK NO.
I'M FINE JUST THE WAY I AM! WHY SHOULD *I* CHANGE?
IN FACT, I THINK IT'S HIGH TIME THE WORLD STARTED CHANGING TO SUIT *ME*! I DON'T SEE WHY *I* SHOULD DO ALL THE CHANGING AROUND HERE!
IF THE NEW YEAR REQUIRES RESOLUTIONS, I SAY IT'S UP TO EVERYONE ELSE, NOT ME! *I* DON'T NEED TO IMPROVE! EVERYONE *ELSE* DOES!
HOW ABOUT YOU? DID YOU MAKE ANY RESOLUTIONS?
WELL, I HAD RESOLVED TO BE LESS OFFENDED BY HUMAN NATURE, BUT I THINK I BLEW IT ALREADY.
WATTERSON

I HATE WAITING FOR THE SCHOOL BUS ON DAYS LIKE THESE.
BLUSTERY COLD DAYS SHOULD BE SPENT PROPPED UP IN BED WITH A MUG OF HOT CHOCOLATE AND A PILE OF COMIC BOOKS.
THAT'S WHAT I'D LIKE TO BE DOING RIGHT NOW.
WATTERSON
AS SOON AS I GRADUATE, I'M GOING TO SPEND ***EVERY*** WINTER THAT WAY.
I WISH YOUR BUS WOULD COME. MY HOT CHOCOLATE WILL GET COLD.

HELP ME FIGURE OUT THIS HOMEWORK PROBLEM, HOBBES. WHAT'S 3+8?
OK, ASSIGN THE ANSWER A VALUE OF "X". "X" ALWAYS MEANS MULTIPLY, SO TAKE THE NUMERATOR (THAT'S LATIN FOR "NUMBER EIGHTER") AND PUT THAT ON THE OTHER SIDE OF THE EQUATION.
THAT LEAVES YOU WITH THREE ON THIS SIDE, SO WHAT TIMES THREE EQUALS EIGHT? THE ANSWER, OF COURSE, IS SIX.
GOSH, I MUST HAVE DONE ALL THE OTHERS WRONG.
THESE PROBLEMS SEEM AWFULLY ADVANCED FOR FIRST GRADE, IF YOU ASK ME.
WATTERSON

HERE'S ANOTHER MATH PROBLEM I CAN'T FIGURE OUT. WHAT'S 9+4?
OOH, THAT'S A TRICKY ONE. YOU HAVE TO USE CALCULUS AND IMAGINARY NUMBERS FOR THIS.
IMAGINARY NUMBERS?!
YOU KNOW, ELEVENTEEN, THIRTY-TWELVE, AND ALL THOSE. IT'S A LITTLE CONFUSING AT FIRST.
HOW DID ***YOU*** LEARN ALL THIS? YOU'VE NEVER EVEN GONE TO SCHOOL!
INSTINCT. TIGERS ARE BORN WITH IT.
WATTERSON

IT'S FREEZING IN THIS HOUSE! SOMEBODY CRANK UP THE THERMOSTAT! WHY DOESN'T SOMEONE MAKE A FIRE?!
IF WE CAN'T AFFORD TO HEAT THIS PLACE, MAYBE DAD SHOULD GET A BETTER JOB! WHY CAN'T WE MOVE TO FLORIDA?!
CALVIN, PIPE DOWN AND PUT ON A SWEATER IF YOU'RE COLD.
AND GO TO ALL THAT TROUBLE?!

I READ THAT THE AVERAGE HOUSEHOLD WATCHES 7½ HOURS OF TV EVERY DAY.
MOM SAYS SHE DOESN'T WATCH TV AT ALL WHILE I'M AT SCHOOL...
...SO IF I GET HOME AT 3:00, I SHOULD BE ABLE TO WATCH IT STRAIGHT TILL 10:30, RIGHT?
WRONG.
DO YOU WANT US TO BE SUB-AVERAGE?!

MOM, THE WASHER IS DONE.
OK.
AREN'T YOU GOING TO PUT THE WASH IN THE DRYER?
IN A MINUTE.
YOU MEAN YOU'RE JUST GOING TO LET IT SIT IN THE WASHING MACHINE?!?
CALVIN, CAN'T YOU SEE I'M BUSY RIGHT NOW?!
SHE SAYS SHE'S BUSY.
I HOPE THE NEXT TIME SHE TAKES A BATH THERE AREN'T ANY TOWELS.

Calvin and Hobbes
by WATTERSON
TWO PARTS SLUSH... ONE PART SOLID ICE... ONE PART HARD-PACKED SNOW... A DASH OF ASSORTED DEBRIS...
SCULPT INTO SPHERE, AND SERVE AT HIGH VELOCITY WITHOUT WARNING.
OH, BOY, HERE COMES SUSIE!
HEY, SUSIE!
WHAP!
HA HA! I GOTCHA, YOU DUMB GIRL!!
AUGHH!
MY EYEBALL! WHERE'S MY EYEBALL?!
WHAT ARE YOU TALKING ABOUT? I HIT YOU IN THE BACK.
IT KNOCKED MY EYEBALL OUT! FIND IT AND PACK IT IN SNOW SO THEY CAN SAVE IT! OW! OW!
GOSH, DID YOU REALLY LOSE YOUR EYEBALL? I DIDN'T KNOW THEY CAME OUT! WOW. I'M REALLY SORRY. I DIDN'T MEAN TO KNOCK IT OUT. CAN I SEE THE SOCKET? BOY, WHERE DO YOU SUPPOSE IT ROLLED?
WATTERSON
SOMEWHERE OVER THERE, POOP HEAD.!!
BOOT
WHAT ARE YOU DOING?
MY EYEBALL FELL OUT. HELP ME LOOK FOR IT.

WHO'S COMING TO VISIT?
YOUR UNCLE MAX. I THOUGHT I TOLD YOU.
UNCLE MAX?? I DON'T REMEMBER ANY UNCLE MAX. ARE YOU SURE HE'S RELATED? MAYBE HE'S A CON MAN TRYING TO SWINDLE US!
OF COURSE HE'S RELATED. HE'S YOUR DAD'S BROTHER. HE JUST HASN'T BEEN HERE FOR A FEW YEARS.
WHY NOT? WAS HE IN JAIL?
NO! GOOD HEAVENS, CALVIN.
NOW, NOW... WITH MAX, THAT'S NOT A BAD GUESS.
WATTERSON

WE'RE GETTING NEAR THE AIRPORT, CALVIN. SEE THE JETS?
HOW COME YOU'RE SO QUIET BACK THERE? AREN'T YOU EXCITED TO SEE UNCLE MAX?
...YEAH...
WATTERSON
I JUST HOPE NOBODY THINKS I'M GIVING UP MY ROOM WHILE HE'S HERE.

IT'S GREAT TO SEE YOU, MAX! IT SEEMS LIKE AGES SINCE YOU'VE BEEN HERE.
I'LL SAY.
I DIDN'T THINK IT HAD BEEN SO LONG, UNTIL I SAW CALVIN. THIS GUY HAS REALLY GROWN.
SO KID, WHAT DO YOU SAY?
I SAY YOU'D BETTER WATCH YOUR STEP, 'CAUSE I'VE GOT A LIVE, MAN-EATING TIGER AT HOME, AND IF I SO MUCH AS WINK, HE'LL RIP YOUR LUNGS OUT.
CUTE KID, BRO.
WATTERSON

AND THIS IS MY ROOM, UNCLE MAX. I DON'T KNOW WHERE YOU'RE SLEEPING, BUT IT SURE ISN'T HERE.
GOTCHA. NICE ROOM.
THIS IS HOBBES. I WOULDN'T GET TOO CLOSE IF I WAS YOU.
DON'T WORRY. HE LOOKS LIKE A FIERCE ONE.
YEP. MANDIBLES OF DEATH, THAT'S WHAT HE'S GOT.
... AND A KILLER'S EYE. YOU CAN TELL. I...I THINK I'LL GO DOWNSTAIRS.
OL' UNCLE MAX SEEMS PRETTY SHARP. HARD TO BELIEVE HE'S RELATED TO DAD.
"A KILLER'S EYE," HE SAID! WOW! I WONDER WHICH ONE!
WATTERSON

HEY!
HEY, KID, WHAT ARE YOU DOING ?!
WATTERSON
I'M GOING THROUGH YOUR LUGGAGE. WHAT'S IT LOOK LIKE I'M DOING?
DID MOMMY AND DADDY RAISE YOU THEMSELVES, OR DID THEY JUST UNTIE YOU FOR MY VISIT?
DIDN'T YOU BRING ME A PRESENT? I CAN'T FIND ONE ANYWHERE.

IS THIS MY PLACE? CAN'T I SIT OVER THERE? I WANT TO SIT NEXT TO UNCLE MAX. CAN I? PLEASE? PLEASE?
OK, GO AHEAD. MOVE YOUR CHAIR OVER.
WATTERSON
YOU SHOULD BE FLATTERED, MAX. CALVIN ASKED TO SIT BY YOU TONIGHT.
HEY, THAT'S SWEET.
THBBPTH-BPT!

DO YOU HAVE ANY KIDS, UNCLE MAX?
ME? NOPE, I'M NOT EVEN MARRIED.
OH.
...WHAT DIFFERENCE DOES **THAT** MAKE?
KID WATCHES A LOT OF TV, DOES HE?

BOY, CALVIN TAKES THAT STUFFED TIGER EVERYWHERE HE GOES.
YEAH, THEY'RE INSEPARABLE.
DO YOU WORRY ABOUT THAT? I MEAN, SHOULDN'T HE BE PLAYING WITH REAL FRIENDS?
OH, I THINK HE WILL WHEN HE'S READY. DIDN'T YOU EVER HAVE AN IMAGINARY FRIEND?
SOMETIMES I THINK **ALL** MY FRIENDS HAVE BEEN IMAGINARY.

UNCLE MAX, LOOK! I'LL SHOW YOU A MAGIC DISAPPEARING TRICK!
OK, FIRST I'LL NEED AN ORDINARY TWENTY-DOLLAR BILL.
HOW ABOUT IF I LEND YOU A NICKEL INSTEAD?
NO, IT WORKS MUCH BETTER WITH A TWENTY. ...OR A FIFTY, IF YOU HAVE ONE.
I TAKE IT YOU THINK YOUR OL' UNCLE MAX IS A LOW-WATT BULB.
WHY, DID DAD TELL YOU HOW THIS WORKS?

WHEN ARE YOU GOING BACK HOME, UNCLE MAX?
TOMORROW. IS THAT SOON ENOUGH?
GEE, I WISH YOU COULD STAY FOREVER.
WHAT A NICE THING TO SAY! YOU'RE ALL RIGHT, CALVIN.
MOM'S A LOT MORE PATIENT WITH ME IN FRONT OF GUESTS.
WATTERSON

WELL, SO LONG, MAX. IT WAS GREAT TO SEE YOU AGAIN.
YOU, TOO.
HAVE A SAFE TRIP HOME.
COME VISIT ME SOMETIME, OK, FELLA?
HECK, I'LL COME RIGHT NOW! SO LONG, MOM! BYE, DAD!
CALVIN, GET BACK HERE!
I NEVER GET TO DO ANYTHING FUN.
MISSED YOUR CHANCE, DEAR. WE COULD'VE BOUGHT HIM A TICKET.
WELL...
WATTERSON

ARE YOU JUST GOING TO SIT INSIDE ALL DAY?
YOU SHOULD GO PLAY OUTSIDE AND GET SOME FRESH AIR!
WATTERSON

Calvin and HOBBES
by WATTERSON
I'VE GOT TO GO IN. ANOTHER FIVE MINUTES OUT HERE, AND I'LL BE FROZEN SOLID.
GOSH, I HOPE THAT WAS NO ONE I KNEW.
YOU LOOKED PRETTY COLD COMING UP THE HILL, SO I FIXED YOU SOME HOT CHOCOLATE AND CRACKERS WITH PEANUT BUTTER.
GO WRAP UP IN A BLANKET AND TAKE THESE IN FRONT OF THE FIRE.
HERE'S HOBBES AND A COMIC BOOK. GETTING TOASTY?
UH HUH. THANKS.
SHE EVEN PUT MARSHMALLOWS IN THE HOT CHOCOLATE.
NOBODY KNOWS HOW TO PAMPER LIKE A MOM.
SO ARE YOU GOING TO EAT ALL THOSE PEANUT BUTTER CRACKERS YOURSELF, OR WHAT?
WATTERSON

Calvin and HOBBES
by WATTERSON
SEVEN.. EIGHT... NINE... TEN!
THAT'S MY SQUARE! HA HA! YOU OWE ME MONEY!
..UH...ELEVEN!
JUST A MINUTE!
WHAT ARE YOU DOING ?!? YOU CAN'T JUST TAKE MONEY FROM THE BANK!
YOU'VE GOT HOTELS ON EVERY PIECE OF PROPERTY YOU OWN. I CAN'T AFFORD TO PAY YOU, SO I'M STICKING UP THE BANK. IT'S A ROBBERY!
YOU CAN'T DO THAT!
I'M THE BANKER, RIGHT? AM I GOING TO RISK MY LIFE OVER A FEW THOUSAND DOLLARS?
THE RULES DON'T SAY YOU CAN ROB THE BANK. THAT'S CHEATING.
DO THE RULES SAY YOU CAN'T ROB THE BANK? HUH? DO THEY? JUST ROLL THE DICE AND ACCEPT THIS AS A TRAGIC TURN OF EVENTS, OK?
OK, IF THAT'S HOW WE'RE PLAYING, THEN I'M ROBBING YOU!
HA! I'LL STEAL YOUR DEEDS TO PARK PLACE AND BOARDWALK!
YEAH? WELL, I'M TAKING ALL THE HOUSES AND HOTELS, AND PUTTING THEM ON BALTIC, WHERE YOU JUST LANDED! YOU OWE ME $ 250,000!
THAT'S WHAT YOU THINK, YOU... YOU...
ISN'T IT CUTE HOW CALVIN PLAYS BOTH SIDES OF MONOPOLY WITH HIS STUFFED TIGER?
I DUNNO... I OVERHEARD HIM USING WORDS HE DIDN'T LEARN IN THIS HOUSEHOLD.
WATTERSON

AAGHH, I CAN'T BELIEVE WE WERE ASSIGNED TO DO A REPORT TOGETHER.
ALL I CAN SAY IS YOU'D BETTER DO A GREAT JOB! I DON'T WANT TO FLUNK JUST BECAUSE I WAS ASSIGNED A DOOFUS FOR A PARTNER.
A DOOFUS ?!? WHO TAKES HER SANDWICHES APART AND EATS EACH INGREDIENT SEPARATELY?
WHAT'S WRONG WITH THAT?!
IT CERTIFIES YOU AS A GRADE "A" NIMROD.
IT DOES NOT!
WATTERSON

OK, LOOK. WE'VE GOT TO DO THIS DUMB PROJECT TOGETHER, SO WE MIGHT AS WELL GET IT OVER WITH. WHAT ARE WE SUPPOSED TO BE DOING?
WEREN'T YOU EVEN PAYING ATTENTION?! WHAT WOULD YOU DO IF I WASN'T HERE TO ASK?!? YOU'D FLUNK AND BE SENT BACK TO KINDERGARTEN, THAT'S WHAT!
WATTERSON
SAYS YOU! I HEARD THAT SOMETIMES KIDS DON'T PAY ATTENTION BECAUSE THE CLASS GOES AT TOO SLOW OF A PACE FOR THEM. SOME OF US ARE TOO SMART FOR THE CLASS.
OH, RIGHT. YOU'RE *TOO* SMART.
BELIEVE IT, LADY. YOU KNOW HOW EINSTEIN GOT BAD GRADES AS A KID? WELL, ***MINE*** ARE EVEN ***WORSE!***

SO WHAT ARE WE SUPPOSED TO BE DOING?
WE'RE ***SUPPOSED*** TO BE RESEARCHING THE PLANET MERCURY.
SO WHAT HAVE WE FOUND OUT?
NOTHING! I'M NOT GOING TO DO THIS WHOLE THING MYSELF!
YOU'D PROBABLY GOOF IT ALL UP IF YOU DID. LET'S GET STARTED.
YES! ***LET'S!***
I'LL BE THE MANAGEMENT, AND YOU CAN BE THE LABOR. FIRST, GET SOME BOOKS.
DOES ANYONE WANT TO TRADE PARTNERS?
WATTERSON

WHAT ARE YOU DOING?! YOU'RE DOODLING! YOU'RE SITTING HERE DRAWING MARTIANS WHEN WE'RE SUPPOSED TO BE RESEARCHING!
YOU HAVEN'T DONE ANYTHING YET! DON'T YOU CARE?? WHAT'S THE MATTER WITH YOU?!
IT'S NO USE! WE'RE GOING TO FLUNK! I'LL HAVE TO GO TO A SECOND-RATE COLLEGE BECAUSE MY IDIOT PARTNER SPENT THE STUDY PERIOD DRAWING MARTIANS!
WHY ME? WHY ME? WHY ME?
HERE, THIS WILL CHEER YOU UP. THE MARTIAN MOVES WHEN YOU FLIP THE PAGES! WATCH, YOU CAN SEE HIM EAT AN ASTRONAUT!
WATTERSON

LOOK, BIRD BRAIN, YOU WASTED THIS ENTIRE WEEK IN THE LIBRARY.
WE HAVE TO GIVE OUR REPORT ON MONDAY. YOU'D BETTER BUST YOUR BUTT OVER THE WEEKEND, OR I'M TELLING THE TEACHER YOU DIDN'T DO ANY WORK. GOT IT?
...WELL, WHAT DO YOU SAY?! AM I GETTING THROUGH TO YOU?? THIS IS IMPORTANT!
GRONK! GRIBBLE GOK! GAK GORK! GOONK!!
OUR HERO REGARDS THE STRANGE ALIEN. ...IT SEEMS TO BE TRYING TO COMMUNICATE.
WATTERSON

CALVIN, TELEPHONE!
WHY AREN'T YOU AT THE LIBRARY?!!?
WATTERSON

WE HAVE TO GIVE OUR REPORT ON PLANET MERCURY TODAY. DID YOU DO YOUR HALF?
OF COURSE I DID. AND I'LL BET MY HALF MAKES YOUR HALF LOOK PATHETIC.
IT HAD BETTER BE GOOD... OR ELSE!
THE PLANET MERCURY
An EXHAUSTIVELY RESEARCHED REPORT BY CALVIN

"..AND SO, THE PLANET MERCURY IS A HOT AND BARREN WORLD, THE CLOSEST TO OUR SUN."
AND TO TELL US ABOUT THE MYTHOLOGY OF MERCURY, HERE'S MY PARTNER, CALVIN.
THANK YOU, THANK YOU! HEY, WHAT A CROWD! YOU LOOK GREAT THIS MORNING...REALLY, I MEAN THAT! GO ON, GIVE YOURSELVES A HAND!
YOU KNOW, A FUNNY THING HAPPENED ON THE WAY TO THE LIBRARY YESTERDAY...
THIS ISN'T MY FAULT, MISS WORMWOOD!

THE PLANET MERCURY WAS NAMED AFTER A ROMAN GOD WITH WINGED FEET.
MERCURY WAS THE GOD OF FLOWERS AND BOUQUETS, WHICH IS WHY TODAY HE IS A REGISTERED TRADEMARK OF FTD FLORISTS.
WHY THEY NAMED A PLANET AFTER THIS GUY, I CAN'T IMAGINE.
...UM... BACK TO YOU, SUSIE.

BOY, YOU SHOULD'VE SEEN THE SPARKS FLY WHEN I GAVE MY HALF OF THE REPORT.
I'VE NEVER SEEN SUSIE SO MAD. SHE ACCUSED ME OF NOT DOING ANY RESEARCH AND CLAIMED I MADE UP THE WHOLE THING.
DID YOU?
HECK, NO. I JUST TOOK A FEW CREATIVE LIBERTIES.
AND THEY CALLED YOUR MOM OVER A FEW CREATIVE LIBERTIES?
GEEZ, YOU THINK SUSIE WAS MAD...

DON'T YOU HATE IT WHEN YOUR BOOGERS FREEZE?

HERE WE ARE, OVERLOOKING SUICIDE GULCH, ABOUT TO HURL OURSELVES DOWN AT BREAKNECK SPEED IN A SLED THAT HARDLY STEERS!
RISKING LIFE AND LIMB! LOOKING DEATH STRAIGHT IN THE EYE!
"WHY?" YOU ASK! WHY DO WE DO IT??
BECAUSE WE GET PAID, I HOPE.
BECAUSE IT'S THERE!

Calvin and Hobbes
by WATTERSON
PLANET BOG — POOLS OF TOXIC CHEMICALS BUBBLE UNDER A CHOKING ATMO-SPHERE OF POISONOUS GASES.
...BUT ASIDE FROM THAT, IT'S NOT MUCH LIKE EARTH.
WE FIND SPACEMAN SPIFF STRUGGLING ACROSS THE TERRAIN OF A DISTANT PLANET!
SUDDENLY THE GROUND BEGINS TO SHAKE! A CLOUD OF DUST APPEARS ON THE HORIZON! IT'S A ZORG!!
OUR HERO RUNS FOR COVER, BUT THE ZORG IS INSTANTLY UPON HIM!
SPIFF FIRES HIS BLASTER, BUT THE WEAPON IS USELESS AGAINST THE MONSTER!
THE FEARLESS SPACE EXPLORER IS TAKEN TO THE ZORG'S CAVE, WHERE HE DISCOVERS A VAT OF BOILING WATER! OH NO! OUR HERO IS ABOUT TO BE COOKED ALIVE!
SPIFF'S MIND RACES FURIOUSLY...
WELL? GET IN.
DON'T YOU WANT TO LEAN WAY, WAY OVER, AND TEST HOW HOT THE WATER IS?
WATTERSON

Calvin and HOBBES
by WATTERSON
I'M GOING OUTSIDE! I'LL BE OUT BACK IF ANYONE WANTS ME! I'LL PROBABLY BE GONE A COUPLE HOURS! I'M LEAVING NOW! I'M GOING! SO LONG! SEE YA LATER! BYE!
STOMP STOMP STOMP STOMP
STOMP STOMP STOMP
HEY SUSIE, LOOK! I FOUND DINOSAUR TRACKS!
WATTERSON
PRETTY SCARY, HUH? I'LL BET YOU DIDN'T KNOW THERE WERE DINOSAURS IN THIS NEIGHBORHOOD!
ESPECIALLY NOT DINOSAURS WITH SIZE 5, TREADED TOES.

LOOK, HOBBES, THE LATEST PERFECTION IN TECHNOLOGY.
A WATER PISTOL?
HECK, NO! THIS IS THE NEW, IMPROVED VERSION OF THE TRANSMOGRIFIER.
NOW YOU CAN TRANSMOGRIFY THINGS JUST BY POINTING AT THEM! SAY YOU DON'T LIKE THE COLOR OF YOUR BEDSPREAD. WELL, YOU JUST ZAP IT, AND PRESTO, IT'S AN IGUANA!
ONE CAN CERTAINLY IMAGINE THE MYRIAD OF USES FOR A HAND-HELD IGUANA MAKER.
IT DOESN'T **HAVE** TO BE AN IGUANA. IT CAN BE ANYTHING. SUPPOSE MOM'S GETTING ON OUR NERVES, FOR INSTANCE...

HOW DOES THIS TRANSMOGRIFIER GUN KNOW WHAT TO TRANSMOGRIFY SOMETHING INTO?
TELEPATHY.
THE GUN AUTOMATICALLY READS THE BRAIN WAVES YOU EMIT, AND TURNS THE OBJECT INTO WHATEVER YOU WANT.
THAT'S AMAZING.
WELL, IT TOOK ME ALL MORNING TO INVENT.
SO SAY I'M THINKING ABOUT A BIG SLAB OF GRILLED TUNA NOW...
WATCH WHERE YOU'RE POINTING THAT! WATCH WHERE YOU'RE POINTING THAT!

OK, LET'S TEST THIS TRANSMOGRIFIER GUN.
I WANT TO BE A PTERODACTYL, SO YOU THINK OF ONE AND POINT THE TRANSMOGRIFIER AT ME.
THIS WILL BE GREAT. I'LL TERRORIZE THE NEIGHBORHOOD AWHILE AND THEN YOU CAN TRANSMOGRIFY ME BACK TO A BOY WHEN THE NATIONAL GUARD COMES.
WHAT'S A PTERODACTYL? SOME KIND OF BUG?
NO NO! IT'S A BIG FLYING DINOSAUR! DON'T SHOOT IF YOU DON'T KNOW WHAT IT IS!!

A CHICKEN ?!' YOU TRANSMOGRIFIED ME INTO A CHICKEN !!'
YOU WERE SUPPOSED TO TURN ME INTO A PTERODACTYL, YOU NINCOMPOOP!!'
ALL YOU HAD TO DO WAS THINK OF A PTERODACTYL! WHY DID YOU THINK OF A CHICKEN ?!?
IT'S ALMOST LUNCHTIME.
OH, I SEE! WELL I'M GLAD YOU WERENT HUNGRY FOR A HOT DOG!
WATTERSON

HERE'S THE TRANSMOGRIFIER GUN. NOW TRY AGAIN, AND DO IT RIGHT. I WANT TO BE A PTERODACTYL.
OK, HERE YOU GO.
ZAP
WELL, NOW, THAT'S MORE LIKE IT!
SAY, WHEN DID YOU TURN YOURSELF INTO A 200-FOOT-TALL COLOSSUS?
I DIDN'T. WHY?
WATTERSON

YOU TRANSMOGRIFIED ME INTO A TINY PTERODACTYL ?!?
BIG DINOSAURS GIVE ME THE WILLIES.
YOU NUMBSKULL! HOW AM I GOING TO TERRORIZE THE NEIGHBORHOOD LIKE THIS ?!'
MY, AREN'T YOU THE CRANKY ONE TODAY?
BY GOLLY, I'LL SHOW YOU!
ZAP
HA HA! SERVES YOU RIGHT!
YOU, MY FRIEND, JUST MADE A BIG MISTAKE.
WATTERSON

Calvin and HOBBES
by WATTERSON
THERE! NOW WE'RE BOTH TRANSMOGRIFIED. WE'RE EVEN!
EVEN?? WE WOULD BE EVEN ONLY IF TURNING A TIGER INTO A DUCK WAS AN IMPROVEMENT.
THIS WASN'T AT ALL WHAT I HAD IN MIND WHEN I ASKED YOU TO TRANSMOGRIFY ME INTO A PTERODACTYL. PTERODACTYLS ARE BIG!
SO YOU TURNED ME INTO A DUCK, IS THAT IT?
FAIR'S FAIR.
OK, I'LL TAKE THE TRANSMOGRIFIER AND FIX YOU UP RIGHT.
ZAP
WHY YOU..!! GIMME THAT GUN!
THBBT!
ZAP
AN INSULT! THIS IS WORSE THAN BEFORE!!
ZAP
ZAP
ZAP
Much Later...
GREAT. JUST GREAT. WHICH OF US IS CALVIN AND WHICH IS HOBBES NOW?
WELL I HOPE CALVIN IS YOU, BECAUSE HIS MOM'S GOING TO HAVE A FIT WHEN SHE SEES THIS.
WATTERSON

LOOK, I'LL TRANSMOGRIFY YOU BACK TO A TIGER IF YOU'LL TRANSMOGRIFY ME BACK TO A KID, OK?
OK.
ZAP
AHH, THAT'S MUCH BETTER.
NOW DO ME.
CLICK...CLICK...CLICK
WHAT'S WRONG?!? I'M NOT TRANSMOG-RIFYING!
BOY, I'M GLAD WE DID ME FIRST.

WHAT'S WRONG WITH THE TRANSMOGRIFIER? WHY WON'T IT WORK?!
YOU INVENTED IT. YOU TELL ME.
DON'T TELL ME I'M STUCK AS AN OWL FOR THE REST OF MY LIFE!
I THINK OWLS MOSTLY EAT MICE. I SUPPOSE WE COULD CATCH SOME IN THE YARD.
THIS IS AWFUL! WHAT AM I GOING TO DO?!
UGGH, I COULD NEVER EAT A MOUSE RAW. THEIR LITTLE FEET ARE PROBABLY REAL COLD GOING DOWN.
WILL YOU FORGET THE STUPID MICE AND HELP ME THINK?!?
I WONDER IF PET STORES WILL SELL YOU A MOUSE IF THEY KNOW YOU'RE GOING TO EAT IT?

HI, MOM, I'M AN OWL.
YOU DON'T LOOK LIKE A VERY *HAPPY* OWL.
NOPE. I'M NOT.
MAYBE SOME LUNCH WOULD HELP.
I DOUBT IT. I DON'T LIKE MICE.
THIS IS SOUP.
IS IT MOUSE SOUP? I DON'T LIKE MICE.
I HEARD YOU. IT'S TOMATO.

WHAT AM I GOING TO DO, HOBBES? I CAN'T BE AN OWL FOREVER!
HOW AM I GOING TO TRANSMOGRIFY BACK INTO A KID WHEN THE TRANS-MOGRIFIER IS BROKEN?
MAYBE YOU SHOULD JUST LEARN TO ACCEPT THIS PREDICAMENT. IT'S NOT SO BAD BEING AN OWL INSTEAD OF A KID. ACTUALLY, IT'S PROBABLY BETTER.
BETTER?! HOW?
WELL, I NEVER QUITE KNEW HOW TO SAY THIS BEFORE, BUT LITTLE BOYS DON'T SMELL SO GOOD.

I'VE GOT TO GO TO SCHOOL TOMORROW MORNING! WHAT WILL THE KIDS SAY IF I'M AN OWL?!
OH, NO, I'M DOOMED! I'M DOOMED!
SINCE WHEN DO OWLS GO TO SCHOOL?
ZIP-A-DEE-DOO-DAH ZIP-A-DEE-AY! MY OH MY, WHAT A WONDERFUL DAY!

TIME TO GET UP, CALVIN. YOU DON'T WANT TO MISS THE SCHOOL BUS.
I'M NOT GOING TO SCHOOL, MOM. I'M AN OWL.
NO, YOU'RE NOT. NOW GET UP AND GET DRESSED.
I'M NOT AN OWL?
I'M NOT! I'M ME AGAIN! THE TRANSMOGRIFICATION MUST ONLY BE TEMPORARY! IT WORE OFF OVERNIGHT! I'M A KID! I CAN...
...GO... TO... SCHOOL.
YAWWWNN.. KEEP THE SHADE DOWN WHEN YOU GO, OK?

Calvin and HOBBES
by WATTERSON
WATTERSON

DING DONG
I'LL GET IT.
WATTERSON
HOBBES, QUICK! CLOSE THE CURTAINS AND HELP ME PROP FURNITURE AGAINST THE DOOR!
..IT'S ROSALYN!

DAD! DAD! WHERE DO YOU KEEP YOUR GUNS? GET OUT THE MAGNUM!
I DON'T HAVE ANY GUNS. WHAT'S THE PROBLEM?
ROSALYN'S HERE AND SHE WON'T GO AWAY! WHY ON EARTH DON'T YOU HAVE ANY GUNS?!?
WATTERSON
YOUR MOM AND I ARE GOING OUT. ROSALYN IS HERE TO BABY-SIT.
DON'T YOU REMEMBER? I TOLD YOU THAT THIS MORNING.
YOU JUST DON'T PAY ATTENTION. THAT'S WHY YOU NEVER KNOW WHAT'S GOING ON.
HOW ABOUT A WOODEN STAKE AND A MALLET? DO WE HAVE THAT?!

CAN YOU BELIEVE IT, HOBBES? MOM AND DAD ASKED ROSALYN TO BABY-SIT US!
THERE'S JUST ONE THING TO DO. WE'LL MAIL OURSELVES TO AUSTRALIA. CLIMB IN.
TO: OS RLYA
JUST PUT US OUT BY THE MAILBOX, MOM.
STOP BEING SILLY, CALVIN. WHERE'S ROSALYN? I THOUGHT YOU SAID SHE WAS HERE.
AS FAR AS I KNOW, SHE'S STILL ON THE FRONT PORCH. WHY?
YOU DIDN'T EVEN LET HER IN?!
DING DONG DING DONG

COME IN, ROSALYN! I'M SORRY! WE DIDN'T REALIZE CALVIN HADN'T LET YOU IN.
THAT'S OK. IT WASN'T *TOO* COLD AND WET OUT.
WE'RE LATE. HELP YOURSELF TO ANYTHING IN THE FRIDGE. WE'LL SEE YOU AT TEN.
THE DOOR WAS JAMMED. REALLY. I COULDN'T GET IT OPEN.
BED.
WATTERSON

HEY, DON'T FIX *THAT* FOR DINNER! DIDN'T MOM TELL YOU HOBBES AND I ARE ON A STRICT BIG MAC DIET? IT'S DOCTOR'S ORDERS!
OH, I'D BETTER CALL YOUR DOCTOR THEN!
OH, NO, SHE CALLED MY BLUFF! THE DOCTOR'S GONNA BE FURIOUS! BOY, ARE WE GOING TO GET IT!
I'M DIALING!
"WE"?
HELLO, DOCTOR? I'M CALLING ABOUT CALVIN'S DIETARY NEEDS.
..AT THE TONE, THE TIME WILL BE 6:27 AND 10 SECONDS.
BEEP
WATTERSON
BAD NEWS, CALVIN. YOUR DOCTOR SAYS YOU SHOULD HAVE A SPOONFUL OF CASTOR OIL AND LIE DOWN ALL EVENING.
HE DID? REALLY? NO, HE DIDN'T. DID HE? WHAT'S CASTOR OIL?

MOM DOESN'T SET THE TABLE THIS WAY. MOM DOES IT A LOT BETTER.
THIS FOOD SMELLS FUNNY. THIS ISN'T THE WAY MOM FIXES IT. I LIKE IT THE WAY MOM DOES IT BETTER.
I'M NOT YOUR MOM, ALL RIGHT?!
WATTERSON
NO KIDDING! MY MOM LOVES ME MORE THAN LIFE ITSELF, AND SHE LETS ME DO ANYTHING I WANT. NOT LIKE *YOU*, YOU NASTY OL' BARRACUDA.
I CAN'T BELIEVE I POSTPONED A DATE FOR THIS.

I'LL GET IT. I THINK IT'S FOR ME.
RING RING
HELLO? ...HI, CHARLIE, THANKS FOR CALLING. ...YEAH, THIS LITTLE FREAK'S DRIVING ME UP THE WALL. ...WHAT? NO, I...
CHARLIE, THIS IS CALVIN ON THE OTHER PHONE! LISTEN TO ME! YOUR GIRLFRIEND'S A SADISTIC KID-HATER! DON'T EVER MARRY HER! SHE'D BE A TERRIBLE MOTHER! SHE...UH OH, GOTTA GO!
AFTER CHARLIE DUMPS YOU, HE'LL THANK ME!

ROSALYN SENT US TO BED AND IT'S NOT EVEN OUR BEDTIME YET!
WE'VE GOT TO ESCAPE.
HERE'S THE PLAN: YOU START MOANING, AND WHEN ROSALYN COMES IN, I'LL THROW THIS BLANKET OVER HER. WE'LL TIE HER UP AND MAKE OUR GETAWAY, GOT IT?
GOT IT.
MROWR YOWOWW RRRR
ROSALYN, COME QUICK! THERE'S SOMETHING WRONG WITH HOBBES!
RIGHT, CALVIN. WHAT SHOULD I DO, CALL A VET?
NO, JUST COME UP HERE AND CLOSE YOUR EYES.

WE'RE HOME! HI, ROSALYN.
HOW WAS CALVIN TONIGHT?
..OH... THAT BAD, EH?
...AND A FIVE DOLLAR ADVANCE ON THE NEXT TIME.
(SIGH) HERE YOU ARE. GOOD NIGHT. THANKS AGAIN.
SHE'S GOT A REAL RACKET GOING, DOESN'T SHE?
WHAT DO YOU WANT TO DO, STAY HOME EVERY NIGHT UNTIL CALVIN'S EIGHTEEN?

Calvin and HOBBES by WATTERSON
"MY....DAD...IS... A...BIG.".. HEY!
WATTERSON
I THINK WE'D BETTER GET THAT KID TO A PSYCHOLOGIST.

Hey, Calvin, guess what we're doing in gym today. We're wrestling!
Next period you'll be so covered with mat burns you'll need skin grafts! Ha ha ha! See ya then, twinky.
SIGHHHHH...
PHYSICAL EDUCATION IS WHAT YOU LEARN FROM HAVING YOUR FACE IN SOMEONE'S ARMPIT RIGHT BEFORE LUNCH.

KAPWIINGGG!
IT'S CALVIN, THE HUMAN LIGHT PARTICLE!
IN THE BLINK OF AN EYE, HE'S 165,000 MILES AWAY!
NOTHING IN THE UNIVERSE IS FASTER THAN CALVIN!
...I HOPE!

MUCH AS I LOVE MY "CHOCOLATE FROSTED CRUNCHY SUGAR BOMBS," THE BEST PART IS AFTER THE CEREAL IS GONE.
THAT'S WHEN YOU EAT THE LEFTOVER MILK THAT'S ALL SLUDGY FROM THE EXTRA SUGAR YOU ADDED.
SOMETIMES I EAT TWO OR THREE BOWLS OF THIS.
I CAN HEAR YOUR HEART RACING FROM HERE.
THEY MAKE THIS CEREAL WITH MARSHMALLOW BITS, TOO, BUT MOM WON'T BUY IT FOR ME.
HEY KIDS!

Calvin and HOBBES
by WATTERSON
IT'S FREEZING UPSTAIRS!
CAN I TAKE SOME LOGS UP TO MY ROOM?
HEY, YOU'RE ON MY SIDE OF THE BED.
THESE SHEETS ARE FREEZING!
YEAH, WELL... AAUGHH! YOUR FEET ARE LIKE ICE! GET AWAY FROM ME!
BUT MY SIDE'S ALL COLD!
WATTERSON
WELL DON'T GET ME COLD! MOVE OVER!
SURE, YOU'VE GOT A FUR COAT! I'M JUST WEARING PAJAMAS.
QUIT PULLING THE BLANKETS, WILLYA?
I HARDLY HAVE ANY, YOU HOG! GIMME THOSE!
YOU'RE LETTING IN COLD AIR! QUIT IT! QUIT IT!
SERVES YOU RIGHT, MR. MOSTY-TOASTY! SEE WHAT IT'S LIKE BEING COLD!
YAAAAH!!!
EAT FEATHERS, FUZZ BALL!
WHAP
OOF
POW
MOVE OVER. YOU'RE GETTING MY SIDE ALL HOT.
OPEN THE WINDOW. I'M ROASTING.

HEY, CALVIN! GUESS WHAT TIME IT IS!
WHY? WHAT TIME IS IT?
IT'S A VERY SPECIAL TIME!
OH BOY, OH BOY! WHAT TIME IS IT?
DO YOU REALLY WANT TO KNOW?
YES, YES! TELL ME! TELL ME! QUICK! PLEASE! YES!
IT'S YOUR BATH TIME! OH BOY!!
YOU KNOW HOW OLD PEOPLE ALWAYS WRITE TO DEAR ABBY, COMPLAINING THAT THEIR KIDS NEVER WRITE, CALL OR VISIT? THOSE LETTERS REALLY CRACK ME UP.
WATTERSON

I HATE BEING A KID.
SOMEBODY'S ALWAYS TELLING YOU WHAT TO DO OR WHAT NOT TO DO. "DO THIS!" "STOP THAT!" DAY AFTER DAY.
YOU'RE LUCKY YOU'RE A TIGER.
WELL, WE TRY TO STAY HUMBLE, BUT LORD KNOWS IT'S HARD.
I WONDER IF I CAN GROW FANGS WHEN MY BABY TEETH FALL OUT.
WATTERSON

I WISH I WAS A TIGER.
A COMMON LAMENT.
I'VE GOT AN IDEA! YOU CAN TEACH ME TO BE A TIGER! I'VE GOT SOME RED SLEEPERS I CAN WEAR! HANG ON!
SEE? WE CAN MAKE A TAIL BY STUFFING A KNEE SOCK AND PINNING IT ON MY REAR! THEN YOU CAN DRAW STRIPES ON MY FACE!
WATTERSON
HMM... WHAT ABOUT FUR AND WHISKERS?
I HAVEN'T SHAVED FOR SIX YEARS. I SEEM TO BE CURSED WITH A THIN BEARD.

GEE, I'M GETTING MORE LIKE A TIGER EVERY MINUTE.
HOLD STILL WHILE I DRAW STRIPES.
HOW DO I LOOK?
IT'S SOME IMPROVEMENT.
ROWRR RRGHGH RAWRR
I DUNNO, YOU'RE STILL LACKING SOMETHING TIGER-ISH.
PANACHE. THAT'S IT.
WAIT, I'VE GOT SOME PLASTIC VAMPIRE FANGS I CAN PUT IN!

THAT'S GREAT, HOBBES! I'M A TIGER!
WELL, BEING A TIGER IS MORE THAN JUST STRIPES, YOU REALIZE.
KIND OF A ZEN THING, HUH?
YOU HAVE TO *THINK* LIKE A TIGER.
"YOWWOW, I'M HUNGRY! WHAT'S FOR DINNER?" ... HOW'S THAT?
HAR HAR. DO YOU WANT ME TO TEACH YOU ANYTHING, OR NOT?

OK, WE'RE TIGERS. WE'RE OUT IN THE WILDERNESS. TEACH ME HOW TO SURVIVE.
LET'S SAY WE'RE HIDING UP IN A TREE. OUR KEEN TIGER EYES AND NOSES DETECT SOME PREY NEARBY. WHAT DO WE DO?
I SUPPOSE IT WOULD DEPEND ON WHAT KIND OF PREY IT WAS.
I DON'T CARE. PICK SOMETHING.
WELL, IF IT'S A BOX OF RIGATONI NOODLES, FIRST YOU WOULD GO PUT ON SOME WATER...

HOBBES, YOU'RE SUPPOSED TO BE TEACHING ME HOW TO BE A TIGER.
WE'VE BEEN SITTING IN THIS DUMB TREE ALL MORNING, AND YOU HAVEN'T TAUGHT ME HOW TO HUNT OR ANYTHING!
IT'S INSTINCT. YOU CAN'T TEACH THAT.
WELL IF YOU WON'T HELP, I'LL JUST GO LOOK UP "TIGER" IN THE ENCYCLOPEDIA.
AS LONG AS WE'RE GOING IN, LET'S FIX SOME SOUP AND SANDWICHES, OK?
YOU KNOW WHAT ***YOU*** ARE? A DISGRACE, THAT'S WHAT.

THIS BOOK SAYS TIGERS ARE SOLITARY AND SECRETIVE CREATURES.
TRUE. VERY TRUE.
SECRETIVE?
OH, SURE! YOU WOULDN'T ***BELIEVE*** SOME OF THE SECRETS I KNOW.
REALLY?? LIKE WHAT?
I CAN'T TELL YOU. THEY'RE SECRETS.
YOU CAN TELL ME! I WON'T BLAB! HONEST! TELL ME! PLEASE??
BIG SECRETS! ***SECRET*** SECRETS! BOY, IF YOU ONLY KNEW! MM-MM!

I DON'T BELIEVE YOU EVEN ***HAVE*** A SECRET.
THAT'S RIGHT. I DON'T.
YES YOU DO! TELL ME IT! PLEEEZE?
NO!
WHY NOT? WHY CAN'T YOU TELL ME??
IT'S ABOUT ***YOU***.
AAAHHH! WHAT IS IT?? TELL ME! TELL ME!
I'VE SAID TOO MUCH ALREADY.

IF YOU WON'T TELL ME YOUR SECRET, I WON'T BE YOUR FRIEND ANY MORE.
I'LL GIVE YOU A HINT, HOW'S THAT?
OK! SHOOT.
THE FLEA MARKET.
"THE FLEA MARKET"?!? WHAT KIND OF LOUSY HINT IS *THAT*?
DO YOU KNOW HOW YOUR PARENTS GOT YOU?
I WAS... *WHY*? WHAT ARE YOU SAYING?
NO MORE HINTS.

I DON'T BELIEVE YOUR DUMB OL' SECRET ABOUT MY PARENTS GETTING ME AT A FLEA MARKET.
IT'S TRUE.
IT IS *NOT*, AND IF *ALL* YOUR SECRETS ARE LIES, YOU CAN JUST KEEP THEM TO YOURSELF.
YOU JUST DON'T WANT TO HEAR HOW LITTLE YOU WENT FOR.
OH, HUSH UP. THIS BOOK ALSO SAYS TIGERS WON'T SHARE THEIR TERRITORY WITH OTHER TIGERS.
TIGERS
I CAN SEE HOW OTHER TIGERS WOULD GET ON ONE'S NERVES.
A NICKEL. THAT'S HOW MUCH YOU COST.

THIS BOOK SAYS TIGERS ARE TERRITORIAL AND WON'T SHARE THEIR GROUND WITH OTHER TIGERS.
I GUESS WE'D BETTER DIVIDE UP THE WOODS THEN. THIS WILL BE MY TERRITORY, AND THAT WILL BE YOURS.
THIS ROCK WILL SEPARATE OUR TWO SIDES. AS ANOTHER TIGER, YOU ARE HEREBY BANISHED FROM THIS SIDE OF THE ROCK.
HA HA HA! LOOK WHAT I-I-I'M DOINGGG!
YOU CUT THAT OUT!

MY SIDE OF THE WOODS ABOUNDS IN NATURAL SCENIC SPLENDOR.
YOUR SIDE WALLOWS IN DECAY AND FILTH. MY TERRITORY IS INFINITELY SUPERIOR TO YOURS.
YOUR SIDE IS SMALLER.
HEY!

I'M HUNGRY.
WELL, YOU CAN'T CATCH ANYTHING IN MY TERRITORY. THAT'S WHAT THE BOOK SAYS.
WHAT DO TIGERS EAT IN THE WILD ANYWAY?
THEY CATCH BIG GROSS CATERPILLARS LIKE THAT ONE.
EWWW. IT'S GOT LITTLE SPIKES ALL OVER HIM. TIGERS REALLY EAT THESE?
BY THE TRUCK LOAD. THEY'RE GREAT.
LET ME SEE THE BOOK.
WHO ARE YOU GOING TO BELIEVE, SOME SILLY WRITER OR A REAL TIGER?

SO FAR, I HAVEN'T HAD MUCH FUN AS A TIGER.
I THOUGHT WE'D BE ROMPING AROUND THE WOODS LIKE WE ALWAYS DO, BUT IT TURNS OUT TIGERS DON'T SHARE THEIR TERRITORIES WITH OTHER TIGERS!
SO HERE WE ARE, SITTING ON OPPOSITE SIDES OF A BIG ROCK. WHAT A BLAST.
BEING A TIGER JUST ISN'T ALL IT'S CRACKED UP TO BE.
THAT'S NOT THE HALF OF IT. IT SAYS HERE WE'RE AN ENDANGERED SPECIES!

WE'RE ENDANGERED?
IT SAYS TIGERS NEARLY FACED EXTINCTION AND THEIR FUTURE REMAINS IN DOUBT.
TIGERS
THAT'S AWFUL.
I'LL SAY.
NO OFFENSE, BUT I THINK I'LL GO BACK TO BEING A KID AGAIN.
THIS EXPLAINS WHY I DON'T MEET MANY BABES.

I'M HOME!
POW
GLAD TO SEE ME??
WHAT I WOULD GIVE TO BE A LATCHKEY KID.

I'M HOME!
WHAM!
YOU'LL NOTICE I DIDN'T SAY I WAS INSIDE.

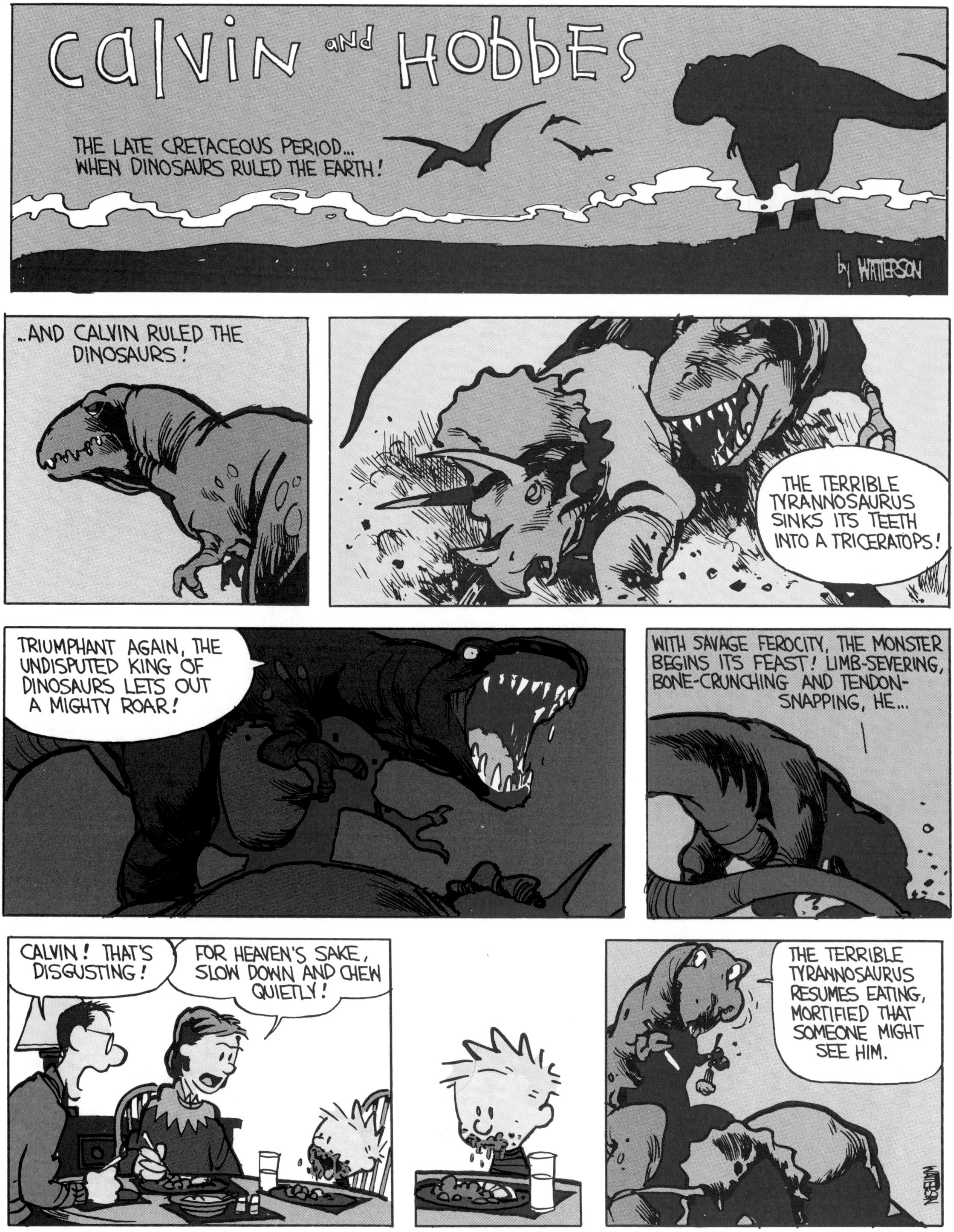
Calvin and Hobbes
THE LATE CRETACEOUS PERIOD... WHEN DINOSAURS RULED THE EARTH!
by WATTERSON
..AND CALVIN RULED THE DINOSAURS!
THE TERRIBLE TYRANNOSAURUS SINKS ITS TEETH INTO A TRICERATOPS!
TRIUMPHANT AGAIN, THE UNDISPUTED KING OF DINOSAURS LETS OUT A MIGHTY ROAR!
WITH SAVAGE FEROCITY, THE MONSTER BEGINS ITS FEAST! LIMB-SEVERING, BONE-CRUNCHING AND TENDON-SNAPPING, HE...
CALVIN! THAT'S DISGUSTING!
FOR HEAVEN'S SAKE, SLOW DOWN AND CHEW QUIETLY!
THE TERRIBLE TYRANNOSAURUS RESUMES EATING, MORTIFIED THAT SOMEONE MIGHT SEE HIM.

Calvin and HobbEs
by WATTERSON
HOOLS
UH OH, I'LL BET HOBBES IS WAITING TO SPRING ON ME AS SOON AS I OPEN THE FRONT DOOR!
I KNOW! I'LL SNEAK AROUND BACK AND SURPRISE ***HIM***!
HEH HEH! THERE HE IS, ALL READY TO POUNCE! WHAT A SUCKER!
I'M HOME!
I'VE GOT TO START LISTENING TO THOSE QUIET, NAGGING DOUBTS.
WATTERSON

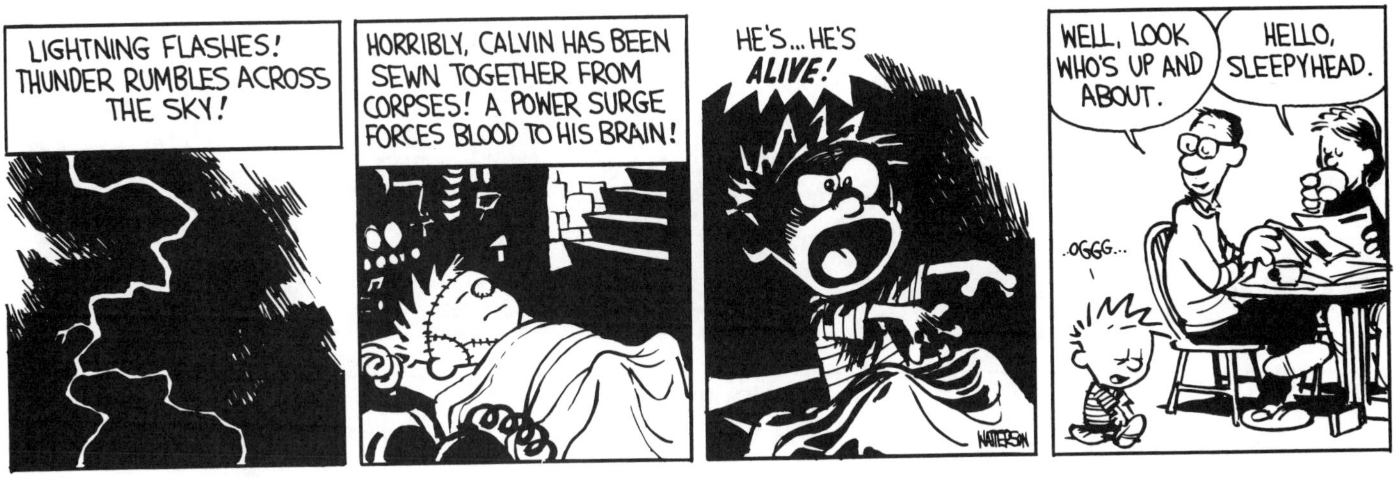
LIGHTNING FLASHES! THUNDER RUMBLES ACROSS THE SKY!
HORRIBLY, CALVIN HAS BEEN SEWN TOGETHER FROM CORPSES! A POWER SURGE FORCES BLOOD TO HIS BRAIN!
HE'S... HE'S **ALIVE!**
WATTERSON
WELL, LOOK WHO'S UP AND ABOUT.
HELLO, SLEEPYHEAD.
..OGGG...

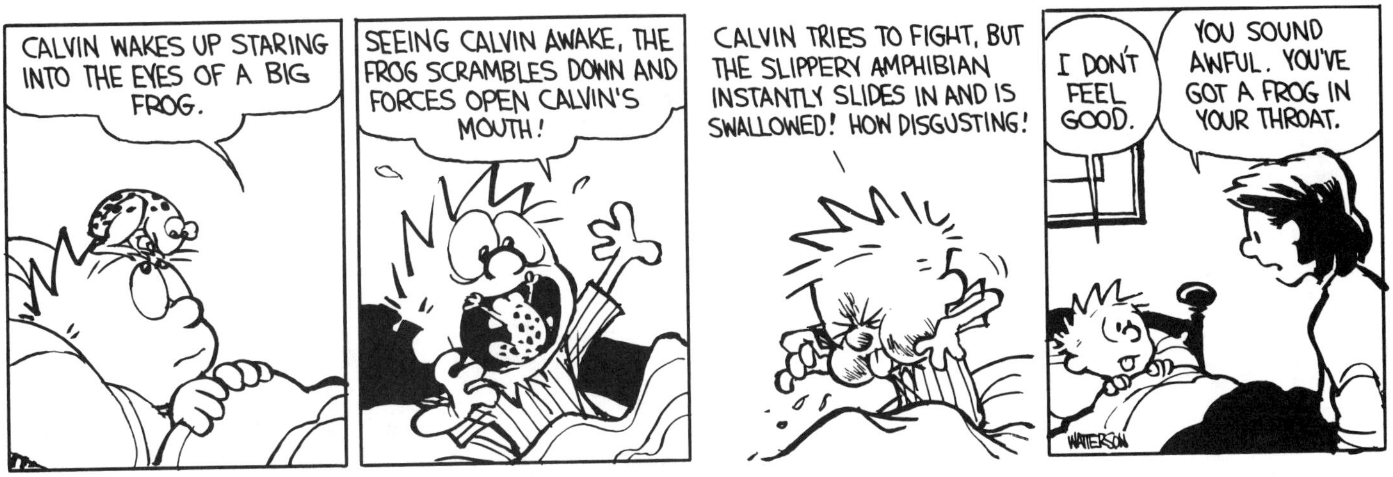
CALVIN WAKES UP STARING INTO THE EYES OF A BIG FROG.
SEEING CALVIN AWAKE, THE FROG SCRAMBLES DOWN AND FORCES OPEN CALVIN'S MOUTH!
CALVIN TRIES TO FIGHT, BUT THE SLIPPERY AMPHIBIAN INSTANTLY SLIDES IN AND IS SWALLOWED! HOW DISGUSTING!
I DON'T FEEL GOOD.
YOU SOUND AWFUL. YOU'VE GOT A FROG IN YOUR THROAT.
WATTERSON

CALVIN THE ELEPHANT WANDERS THE AFRICAN PLAIN.
AT FIVE TONS, HE IS THE LARGEST LAND MAMMAL!
HIS DEAFENING CALL SHATTERS THE EARLY-MORNING TRANQUILITY!
WATTERSON

Calvin and Hobbes
by WATTERSON
A RED SPACESHIP ON THE MONITOR, YOUR VILENESS.
IT'S THAT INFERNAL SPACEMAN SPIFF! OPEN FIRE!
SPACEMAN SPIFF IS HIT! HE AIMS FOR PLANET MOK, HOPING TO FIND A REPUTABLE BODY SHOP.
WE JOIN OUR HERO AFTER A CRASH LANDING ON THE HOSTILE PLANET MOK. OMINOUS FIGURES APPEAR ON THE HORIZON!
THE DARING SPACEMAN SPIFF LAYS WASTE WITH HIS DEATH RAY ZORCHER, BUT HE IS HOPELESSLY OUTNUMBERED!
SURROUNDED, OUR HERO IS TAKEN PRISONER, AND CARRIED TO A SUBTERRANEAN DUNGEON!
STILL WON'T TALK, EH, SPIFF? WE'LL SEE ABOUT *THAT*!
YOU'LL NEVER GET ANYTHING FROM ME, SPACE SQUID!
!
YOU HAD YOUR CHANCE, EARTHLING! TAKE HIM TO THE INTERROGATION ROOM AND ***WASH HIS HAIR***!
HA HA HA HA HA HA HA
AAUGH! YOU GOT SOAP IN MY EYES ON PURPOSE! SINISTER FIEND!
IF YOU'D STOP THRASHING AROUND, MAYBE IT WOULDN'T HAPPEN!
WATTERSON

I READ THAT A CHEETAH CAN RUN 65 MILES AN HOUR.
CAN TIGERS RUN THAT FAST?
OF COURSE.
REALLY? LET'S SEE YOU DO IT.
OH, I CAN'T NOW.
YEAH? WHY NOT?
I'M NOT WEARING MY DRAG CHUTE.

WHY DO YOU SUPPOSE WE'RE HERE?
BECAUSE WE WALKED HERE.
NO, NO... I MEAN HERE ON EARTH.
BECAUSE EARTH CAN SUPPORT LIFE.
NO, I MEAN WHY ARE WE ANYWHERE? WHY DO WE EXIST?
BECAUSE WE WERE BORN.
FORGET IT.
I WILL, THANK YOU.

SATURDAY IS THE BEST DAY OF THE WEEK.
MILK
NO DEMANDS AT ALL!
PERFECT FREEDOM!
THE WHOLE DAY STRETCHES BEFORE US WITH UNLIMITED OPPORTUNITY!
AND WHAT BETTER WAY TO APPRECIATE THAT OPPORTUNITY THAN BY SQUANDERING IT WATCHING CARTOONS ALL DAY!

Calvin and HOBBES
by WATTERSON
WILL YOU GET ME A GLASS OF WATER?
YOU JUST HAD ONE.
I WANT ONE TO KEEP BY THE BED, SO I CAN DOUSE THIS GUY IF HE STARTS SNORING.
GOOD NIGHT, CALVIN.
Z
HEE HEE HEE HEE
OH, GREAT. HE'S DREAMING AGAIN.
SNIFF SNIFF SNIFF
WHERE DO YOU THINK YOU ARE, YOU IMBECILE? OUT IN THE JUNGLE?
...MM... HEH HEH HEH
IF HE STARTS "RUNNING," HE'S GONNA GET A PILLOW IN THE KISSER.
SNIFF SNIFF
HEY! WHERE ARE YOU GOING??
SOMNAMBULISTS GIVE ME THE CREEPS. WHY ARE WE GOING TO THE KITCHEN?
Z
CALVIN! WHAT ARE YOU DOING? HAVE YOU BEEN SLEEPWALKING??
I WAS COMPLETELY AWAKE! IT'S THIS DOPE WHO'S SLEEPWALKING! I JUST FOLLOWED HIM.
I PUT HIM BACK TO BED. HE COULDN'T GIVE ANY REASON FOR BEING UP.
DO YOU SUPPOSE IT MEANS ANYTHING? LOOK, HE GOT OUT ALL THE TUNA!

AHH! LUNCH, MY FAVORITE MEAL! AND TODAY'S LUNCH IS **EXTRA** SPECIAL!
EVER SINCE THE WEATHER GOT WARM I'VE BEEN SWATTING FLIES AND SAVING THEM IN A JAR.
WATTERSON
FINALLY I GOT ENOUGH BUGS TO MASH THEM INTO A GOOEY PASTE WITH A SPOON.
I CALL IT "BUG BUTTER." CARE FOR A TASTE?
TELL ME, CALVIN, DO YOU HAVE ANY FRIENDS AT **ALL**?

OK, YOU'VE ALL READ THE CHAPTER, SO WHO CAN TELL ME WHAT'S IMPORTANT ABOUT THE BATTLE OF LEXINGTON?
7
+5
ANYONE?
CALVIN, HOW ABOUT YOU?
HARD TO SAY, MA'AM. I THINK MY CEREBELLUM JUST FUSED.
WATTERSON

HEY, MOM, CAN WE GO OUT FOR HAMBURGERS TONIGHT?
NOT TONIGHT, DEAR.
AW, MOM! WHY NOT?
BECAUSE I'M ALREADY FIXING SOMETHING FOR DINNER.
WATTERSON
YEAH... I KNOW.

WHY DOES THE SUN SET?
IT'S BECAUSE HOT AIR RISES. THE SUN'S HOT IN THE MIDDLE OF THE DAY, SO IT RISES HIGH IN THE SKY.
IN THE EVENING THEN, IT COOLS DOWN AND SETS.
WHY DOES IT GO FROM EAST TO WEST?
SOLAR WIND.
DEAR!
WATTERSON

I'M THINKING OF A NUMBER BETWEEN ONE AND SEVEN HUNDRED BILLION. TRY TO GUESS IT.
ELEVEN?
NOPE. GUESS AGAIN.
SIX MILLION AND FOUR.
NOPE. GUESS AGAIN.
WHAT'S THE MATTER, DON'T YOU LIKE GAMES ??
WATTERSON

DO YOU BELIEVE OUR DESTINIES ARE DETERMINED BY THE STARS?
NAH.
OH, I DO.
REALLY? HOW COME?
LIFE'S A LOT MORE FUN WHEN YOU'RE NOT RESPONSIBLE FOR YOUR ACTIONS.
WATTERSON

Calvin and HOBBES
by WATTERSON
YAWWNN
!
DESPITE THAT AMAZING DISPLAY OF CUNNING, REFLEX AND PHYSICAL PROWESS, YOUR TAIL STILL HAS A DEATH GRIP ON YOUR BUTT.
COULD YOU STOP THE ROOM, PLEASE? I'D LIKE TO GET OFF.
WATTERSON

BAD NEWS ON YOUR POLLS, DAD. YOU DROPPED ANOTHER FIVE POINTS.
IT SEEMS THAT ALTHOUGH YOUR RECOGNITION FACTOR IS HIGH, THE SCANDALS OF YOUR ADMINISTRATION CONTINUE TO HAUNT YOU.
SCANDALS? WHAT SCANDALS?!
BEDTIMEGATE AND HOMEWORKGATE COME READILY TO MIND.
INSTANCES OF TRUE LEADERSHIP. HISTORY WILL VINDICATE ME.
I WONDER WHAT MY NEW DAD WILL LOOK LIKE.

YOU'LL BE GLAD TO KNOW I'VE ANALYZED YOUR POOR SHOWING IN THE POLLS.
I'LL BET.
SEE, YOUR RECORD IN OFFICE IS MISERABLE AND THE CHARACTER ISSUE IS KILLING YOU. YOUR BASIC APPROVAL RATING AMONG SIX-YEAR-OLDS HARDLY REGISTERS.
IF ANYONE EVER NEEDED A SLICK AD CAMPAIGN, IT'S YOU.
LET ME GUESS WHAT YOU HAVE IN MIND.
"THE NEW DAD" I CALL IT.

I THINK THE IMAGE WE NEED TO CREATE FOR YOU IS, "REPENTANT, BUT LEARNING."
YOU KNOW, SHOW SOME HUMILITY, AND PRESENT YOURSELF AS A REGULAR GUY TRYING TO LEARN THE ROPES OF A DIFFICULT JOB.
DIFFICULT DOESN'T BEGIN TO DESCRIBE IT.
I WORKED UP SOME SLOGANS. SEE WHAT YOU THINK.
"DAD-GRADUALLY, HE CATCHES ON." "VOTE DAD! THIS TIME, HE'LL DO BETTER." "TO FORGIVE IS DIVINE-VOTE DAD IN '88."
I GET THE IDEA, CALVIN.

IF YOU WANT TO STAY DAD, YOU'VE GOT TO POLISH YOUR IMAGE.
MY IMAGE.
RIGHT. SEE, NOW EVERYONE THINKS YOU'RE INSENSITIVE TO THE LEGITIMATE NEEDS OF MINORS.
A FEW MAGNANIMOUS GESTURES WHILE IN OFFICE NOW MIGHT BE IN ORDER. IF YOUR MIND'S GONE BLANK, I HAVE SOME SUGGESTIONS.
OH, THE SUSPENSE.
FOR EXAMPLE, YOU MIGHT REPEAL MANDATORY SCHOOL ATTENDANCE. THAT ALONE COULD ROCKET YOU TO VICTORY.

MUCH AS I APPRECIATE YOUR OFFER, I DON'T THINK I NEED AN IMAGE CONSULTANT.
I PREFER TO LET THE WISDOM OF MY WORDS AND DEEDS SPEAK FOR THEMSELVES.
IN THAT CASE, YOU'LL HAVE A LOT OF TIME TO WRITE YOUR MEMOIRS.
WE'LL SEE. NOW IT'S PAST YOUR BEDTIME.
"DAD BURIED IN LANDSLIDE! JUBILANT THRONGS FILL STREETS! STUNNED FATHER INCONSOLABLE– DEMANDS RECOUNT!"
GOOD NIGHT.

EIGHT... NINE... TEN! HERE I COME, READY OR NOT!
ALL RIGHT, GIVE 'EM BACK!
COMICS

Calvin and Hobbes
by WATTERSON
YES, YOU CAN CERTAINLY SEE FAR FROM UP HERE.
I CALL THIS "LOOKOUT" HILL.
I CALL IT "LOOKOUT" HILL BECAUSE THAT'S WHAT YOU YELL WHENEVER WE GO DOWN IT.
YOU KNOW, SOMETIMES IT SEEMS THINGS GO BY TOO QUICKLY.
WE'RE SO BUSY WATCHING OUT FOR WHAT'S JUST AHEAD OF US THAT WE DON'T TAKE THE TIME TO ENJOY WHERE WE ARE.
DAYS GO BY AND WE HARDLY NOTICE THEM. LIFE BECOMES A BLUR.
OFTEN IT TAKES SOME CALAMITY TO MAKE US LIVE IN THE PRESENT.
THEN SUDDENLY WE WAKE UP AND SEE ALL THE MISTAKES WE'VE MADE, BUT IT'S TOO LATE TO CHANGE ANYTHING.
IT'S LIKE... ...IT'S LIKE...
IT'S LIKE WHAT?
IT'S LIKE SOMETHING... I JUST CAN'T THINK OF IT.

HERE I AM, WAITING FOR THE BUS. ELEVEN MORE YEARS OF SCHOOL TO GO. THEN COLLEGE, THEN MAYBE GRADUATE SCHOOL, AND THEN I WORK UNTIL I DIE.
WHAT KIND OF WORLD IS THIS?! YOU ONLY GET FIVE YEARS TO BE A KID?!
WHAT ABOUT EXPLORING AND DISCOVERING AND PLAYING? THOSE THINGS ARE IMPORTANT, TOO!
WELL, YOU STILL HAVE AFTERNOONS AND WEEKENDS.
THAT'S WHEN I WATCH TV.

LOOK, HOBBES, I GOT A MODEL AIRPLANE. WANT TO HELP ME BUILD IT?
SURE.
WOW, A PHANTOM JET! I CAN'T WAIT UNTIL IT'S DONE!
LOOK AT ALL THE LITTLE PIECES.
HERE, YOU PUT THOSE PIECES TOGETHER, AND I'LL DO THESE. THEN WE'LL STICK YOURS ON MINE, OK?
SHOULDN'T WE READ THE INSTRUCTIONS?
DO I LOOK LIKE A SISSY?

HEY, THESE INSTRUCTIONS ARE IN THREE DIFFERENT LANGUAGES.
UH OH, I GOT GLUE ON MY HANDS.
IT STARTS IN ENGLISH, BUT THEN IT GOES INTO FRENCH AND SPANISH.
THIS STUFF IS WORSE THAN MOZZARELLA CHEESE.
IT'S HARD TO BELIEVE THIS MODEL IS FOR AGES SIX AND UP.
YECCHH. WHAT A MESS.
YOU HAVE TO BE TRI-LINGUAL JUST TO READ THE DIRECTIONS.
I HOPE MOM LIKES THIS NEWSPAPER HERE ON THE FLOOR, BECAUSE IT'S SURE NOT GOING ANYWHERE.

NUTS! THIS WHEEL STRUT SNAPPED. WHY DO THEY MAKE 'EM SO DARN SMALL?
I GUESS THAT WAS AN OPTIONAL PIECE.
MY WHEEL WON'T FIT IN THE WHEEL WELL.
HERE, LET ME TRY. SOMETIMES YOU JUST HAVE TO...
SNAP
DARN IT!
THIS PLANE IS IN FOR SOME ROUGH LANDINGS.

LOOK AT THIS STUPID MODEL. IT LOOKS AWFUL!
OUR PLANE DOESN'T LOOK ANYTHING LIKE THE PICTURE ON THE BOX.
MAYBE WE CAN FIX IT WHEN WE PAINT IT.
I CAN'T PAINT IT LIKE THIS. LOOK HOW GOOD THEY DID THIS!
Phantom
HOW'D THEY PAINT EYEBROWS ON A PILOT THAT'S LESS THAN AN INCH TALL ?!?
I THINK THAT'S A REAL JET SUPERIMPOSED ON A PLASTIC STAND.
WATERSON

I HATE THIS MODEL. NOTHING FIT RIGHT, THE INSTRUCTIONS WERE INCOMPREHENSIBLE, THE DECALS RIPPED, THE PAINT SLOPPED, AND THE GLUE GOT EVERYWHERE.
WHAT A DISASTER. SIX BUCKS COMPLETELY DOWN THE DRAIN.
I CAN'T THINK OF AN AFTERNOON I'VE ENJOYED LESS. WHAT A WASTE. WHAT A DUMB HOBBY.
..OF COURSE, WITH THIS FOR PRACTICE, I'LL BET WE COULD DO GREAT ON ANOTHER MODEL!
LET'S GET ONE OF THOSE CLIPPER SHIPS WITH ALL THE RIGGINGS.

Calvin and HOBBES
by WATTERSON
A VOICE CACKLES IN CALVIN'S RADIO. "ENEMY FIGHTERS AT TWO O'CLOCK!"
ROGER. WHAT SHOULD I DO UNTIL THEN?
CALVIN'S F-4 PHANTOM SCREAMS ACROSS THE SKY!
BUT WHAT'S THIS? THE CANOPY GLASS IS ALL SMEARED! HE CAN HARDLY SEE THROUGH IT!
OH, NO! THE THROTTLE SNAPS OFF IN HIS HAND!
CALVIN'S ONLY HOPE IS TO LAND, BUT THE WHEELS REFUSE TO OPEN! THEY'RE STUCK!
FRANTICALLY CALVIN TRIES TO EJECT, BUT THE COCKPIT IS FUSED TOGETHER! HIS JET IS A HOPELESS MESS! EVERYTHING IS GOING WRONG!
WATTERSON
STUPID MODEL.

I'M NOT GOING TO BED! I DON'T HAVE TO DO WHAT YOU SAY! I CAN DO ANYTHING I WANT!
..UH... HEH HEH
ENJOY THIS WHILE YOU CAN! I'LL BE A HULKING, SURLY TEEN-AGER BEFORE YOU KNOW IT!!

DID YOU EVER WONDER IF THE PERSON IN THE PUDDLE IS REAL, AND YOU'RE JUST A REFLECTION OF HIM?
IF THAT WAS TRUE, YOU'D DISAPPEAR AS SOON AS THE PERSON IN THE PUDDLE MOVED AWAY FROM THE PUDDLE, RIGHT?
GEE, I GUESS SO. I HADN'T THOUGHT OF THAT.

BANG!
BANG! BANG!
HA! THAT'S SIX SHOTS! YOU'RE OUT OF BULLETS! I'VE GOT YOU NOW, YOU RUSTLER!
ZAP!
"ZAP"?
MY CATTLE PROD.

HEY, SUSIE, GUESS WHAT I HAVE IN MY HANDS!
IS IT DISGUSTING?
UM... ..WELL...
IS IT SOME CREEPY, GOOEY THING THAT NO ONE IN HIS RIGHT MIND WOULD EVER, EVER WANT TO LOOK AT?
UH... I SUPPOSE THAT DEPENDS ON YOUR POINT OF VIEW...
FORGET IT. I'M NOT GUESSING.
YOU MIGHT AS WELL. YOU'RE NINE-TENTHS THERE.

MOM, WAS I EVER A GRUB?
A WHAT?
YOU KNOW, A LARVA. DID I REALLY PUPATE AT AGE TWO?
DON'T BE DISGUSTING! OF COURSE NOT! WHERE DID YOU EVER GET THAT AWFUL IDEA?!
YOU SHOULD GET YOUR STORIES STRAIGHT WITH MOM, MR. BRITANNICA!

HOW CAN YOU STAND THESE CARTOONS?
THEY'RE JUST HALF-HOUR COMMERCIALS FOR TOYS. AND WHEN THEY'RE NOT BORING, THEY'RE PREACHY.
AND THESE CHARACTERS DON'T EVEN MOVE. THEY JUST STAND AROUND BLINKING! WHAT KIND OF CARTOON IS THAT?
MEET MY DAD, THE GENE SISKEL OF SATURDAY MORNING TV.

Calvin and HOBBES
by WATTERSON
C'MON, HOBBES. LET ME UP INTO THE TREE FORT.
SAY THE PASSWORD.
NO! YOU KNOW IT'S ME! LET ME UP!
YOU MAY BE SOME OTHER KID IN DISGUISE.
IT'S ME, CALVIN! LET ME UP, YOU HAIRBALL BARFER!
AN INSULT! WELL, YOU CAN JUST STAY DOWN THERE FOREVER, MR. STINKER.
OH, NO! HERE COMES SUSIE! LET ME UP QUICK, SO WE CAN THROW THINGS AT HER! HURRY! LET DOWN THE ROPE!
LA DE DA DUM DOO
SHE'S COMING! QUICK! LET DOWN THE ROPE! I'M SORRY I INSULTED YOU! OK? SEE, I SAID I WAS SORRY! CAN'T YOU LET DOWN THE ROPE?!
YOU HAVE TO SAY THE PASSWORD.
..Verse Seven: TIGERS ARE PERFECT, THE E-PIT-O-ME OF GOOD LOOKS AND GRACE AND QUIET..UH..UM..DIGNITY.
I WAS GOING TO ASK YOU TO COME OVER AND PLAY HOUSE, BUT I THINK YOU'D BE A WEIRD EXAMPLE FOR OUR CHILDREN.
ONE OF THESE DAYS I'M GOING TO MAKE YOU INTO A RUG! YOU HEAR ME?? A RUG!
WATTERSON

CAN I USE THE GARDEN SHOVEL?
WHAT DO YOU WANT IT FOR?
HOBBES AND I ARE GOING ON AN ARCHAEOLOGICAL EXPEDITION.
IF YOU'RE LOOKING FOR FOSSILIZED REMAINS, YOU SHOULD DIG THROUGH YOUR ROOM.
HA HA. SOMEDAY I'LL NAME AN AUSTRALOPITHECUS WOMAN AFTER YOU.

I'VE BEEN READING UP ON PALEONTOLOGY. IT'S AMAZING STUFF.
SCIENTISTS CAN TELL HOW OLD SOMETHING IS JUST BY ANALYZING THE LAYERS OF DIRT IT'S IN.
HEY!
WHY, YOU MUST BE SIX YEARS OLD.
OH, YOU'RE A SCREAM.

ARCHAEOLOGISTS DIG SLOWLY AND CAREFULLY, USING SMALL, DELICATE TOOLS.
EACH ROCK HAS TO BE PAINSTAKINGLY BRUSHED AND SCRAPED SO NOTHING IS BROKEN OR MISSED.
DIG DIG SCRAPE SCRAPE BRUSH BRUSH
ARCHAEOLOGISTS HAVE THE MOST MIND-NUMBING JOB ON THE PLANET.
I DON'T THINK YOUR DAD WILL WANT TO SHAVE WITH THIS TOMORROW.

HEY, LOOK! I HIT SOMETHING!
DON'T BREAK IT! DIG CAREFULLY!
GOSH, WHAT DO YOU SUPPOSE IT IS?
DUST IT OFF SO WE CAN SEE.
IT'S SOME BIZARRE SKULL!
LOOK AT ITS MOUTH. MAYBE IT'S A PREHISTORIC ANTEATER.

WOW! I CAN'T BELIEVE WE FOUND A DINOSAUR SKULL ON OUR VERY FIRST ARCHAEOLOGICAL DIG!
IT'S COMPLETELY INTACT, TOO! WHAT A DISCOVERY!
MAYBE THE REST OF THE SKELETON IS NEARBY!
YEAH! IF WE CAN FIND THE WHOLE THING, WE'LL BE WORLD FAMOUS!
WITH THE GRANT MONEY WE'LL GET, WE CAN BUY A PORSCHE!
HOW WILL **THIS** LOOK ON THE COVER OF NATIONAL GEOGRAPHIC?

I FOUND ANOTHER BONE! I FOUND ANOTHER BONE!
BOY, THIS IS A WEIRD ONE. WHAT IS IT?
IT COULD BE A FOREARM AND FINGERS.
I CAN'T WAIT TO SEE WHAT THE COMPLETE CALVINOSAUR LOOKS LIKE.
I DIDN'T KNOW BONES CAME IN DECORATOR COLORS, DID YOU?

GOSH, LOOK AT ALL THE DINOSAUR BONES WE DISCOVERED.
LET'S GLUE THEM TOGETHER SO WE CAN SEE HOW THEY FIT. THEN YOU CAN DRAW A RECONSTRUCTION OF THE ACTUAL DINOSAUR.
AFTER THAT, WE'LL WRITE UP OUR FINDINGS, AND GET THEM PUBLISHED IN A SCIENTIFIC JOURNAL.
THEN WE'LL WIN THE NOBEL PRIZE, GET RICH, AND GO ON TALK SHOWS.
WHAT ABOUT BABES? WHEN DO WE GET THOSE?
WATTERSON

WELL, HERE'S THE COMPLETE SKELETON AS NEAR AS **I** CAN FIGURE OUT.
TRY TO DRAW THE DINOSAUR AS IT REALLY LOOKED WITH MUSCLES AND SKIN.
RIGHT.
WATTERSON
WHAT'S IT DOING? WHISTLING?
YOU TELL ME. MAYBE IT'S PUCKERING UP.

SEE THE DINOSAUR SKELETON WE DISCOVERED AND ASSEMBLED?
I'M GOING TO CALL THE NATURAL HISTORY MUSEUM AND TELL THEM THEY CAN HAVE IT FOR TEN BILLION DOLLARS.
THOSE ARE ...UM... PECULIAR BONES.
WATTERSON
DO YOU THINK I SHOULD ASK FOR MORE MONEY?
THAT'S NOT ***QUITE*** WHAT I MEANT.

MOM SAYS SHE DOESN'T THINK WE'VE FOUND A SKELETON AT ALL.
SHE SAYS WE JUST DUG UP SOME TRASH SOMEBODY LITTERED.
OUR DINOSAUR IS A FRAUD.
I GUESS IT WOULDN'T BE RIGHT TO SELL IT TO A MUSEUM THEN.
NOT AT FULL PRICE, ANYWAY.

PSST...SUSIE! CAN I COPY YOUR PAPER?
NO.
CALVIN!

AAAUGHH!
I SKINNED MY KNEE!
OOH!
OW!
AAUGHHH!
OW! OW!

Calvin and HOBBES
by WATTERSON
THE CALL GOES OUT! WE'RE ON THE MOVE!
UP THROUGH THE WINDING MAZE! FASTER! FASTER!
CALVIN SCRAMBLES UP THE GRAINY TUNNEL!
OUT HE POPS INTO THE BLINDING SUN! CALVIN THE ANT RUSHES DOWN THE HILL TO THE BRICK WALK!
OTHER ANTS RUSH AROUND HIM IN THEIR MAD HURRY! CALVIN TRIES TO KEEP UP!
AT LAST HE REACHES THE MONSTROUS DEAD CATERPILLAR! WITHOUT PAUSING, HE HOISTS IT UP!
THE QUEEN DEMANDS HIS TIRELESS TOIL! CALVIN IS BACK OFF TO THE ANT-HILL AS FAST AS HE CAN GO!
WORK, WORK, WORK! THAT'S ALL I'M GOOD FOR AROUND HERE!
I HARDLY THINK PICKING UP YOUR ROOM ONCE IN A WHILE QUALIFIES YOU AS A SLAVE.
WATTERSON

Calvin and HOBBES
by WATTERSON
THIS IS CALVIN, YOUR CAPTAIN, SPEAKING...
...JUST TO REASSURE YOU THAT, YES, THERE IS SOMEONE UP FRONT.
CALVIN PILOTS THE JET AIRLINER ACROSS THE COUNTRY AT 35,000 FEET.
HE IS GIVEN CLEARANCE TO LAND. BUT WHAT'S THIS? A PLANE FROM A RIVAL AIRLINE IS MAKING FOR THE SAME RUNWAY TO SHAVE PRECIOUS MINUTES OFF ITS SCHEDULE!
WATTERSON
IT'S A 600-MPH GAME OF CHICKEN! CALVIN PULLS BACK ON THE THROTTLE AND LURCHES AHEAD!
THE OTHER PILOT TRIES TO CUT CALVIN OFF WITH A SUDDEN DROP IN ALTITUDE!
CALVIN SWITCHES ON THE "FASTEN SEAT BELT" LIGHT IN THE CABIN, AND DOES A BARREL ROLL!
AT 5 Gs, CALVIN HOPES NOT TO BLACK OUT!
AS THEY CLOSE IN ON THE RUNWAY, THE OTHER PILOT HAS NO CHOICE BUT TO PULL UP AND CIRCLE AROUND AGAIN! CALVIN WINS!
HEY, MOM, IS IT TRUE I COULD GET A PILOT'S LICENSE AT AGE 14?
NO.

HOBBES! YOU'VE GOT TO HELP ME! I'M IN BIG TROUBLE!
WHAT'S THE MATTER?
YOU KNOW HOW DAD SAID I COULD USE HIS BINOCULARS AS LONG AS I WAS EXTRA CAREFUL WITH THEM? WELL, I JUST BROKE THEM BY ACCIDENT!
NOW I NEED SOME ADVICE. SHOULD I RUN AWAY, OR COMMIT HARA-KIRI?
OVER THE BINOCULARS?
YEAH.
MAYBE BOTH.

GEEZ, I CAN'T BELIEVE I BROKE DAD'S BINOCULARS! HE'LL BLOW EVERY CAPILLARY IN HIS BODY!
DAD SAID I HAD TO BE VERY, VERY CAREFUL WITH THEM, AND WHAT DO I DO? I GO AND BREAK THEM. HE'LL FLAY ME ALIVE!
HOW DID YOU DO IT, ANYWAY?
I JUST DROPPED THEM.
AND THEY BROKE?
WELL, I WAS TOSSING THEM TO MYSELF AT THE TIME, AS I RAN DOWN THE SIDEWALK.

HOW MUCH MONEY DO YOU HAVE, HOBBES? MAYBE WE CAN BUY DAD A NEW PAIR OF BINOCULARS BEFORE HE GETS HOME.
I'VE GOT THIRTY... NO, THIRTY-FIVE CENTS.
GREAT. I'VE GOT FOUR DOLLARS. LET'S CALL THE STORE.
HELLO? I'D LIKE TO KNOW HOW MUCH A GOOD PAIR OF BINOCULARS COSTS.
ONE TO SIX HUNDRED DOLLARS?! DO YOU HAVE ANY IDEA WHAT MY DAD'S GOING TO DO TO ME?!?
HE WON'T STOP AT KILLING YOU, THAT'S FOR SURE. UH HUH.

I HAD NO IDEA BINOCULARS WERE SO EXPENSIVE! WE'RE DOOMED! WE'RE DOOMED!
"WE"?
WHY IN THE WORLD DID DAD LET ME USE ANYTHING SO VALUABLE?! HE SHOULD'VE KNOWN I'D BREAK THEM! HE MUST'VE BEEN OUT OF HIS MIND! THIS IS ALL HIS FAULT!
WHAT AM I GONNA DO?!
I SUPPOSE YOU COULD JUST TELL HIM WHAT HAPPENED...
..AND MAKE MY GETAWAY WHEN THE CORONARY HITS? SAY, THAT'S AN IDEA!
WATTERSON

MAYBE WE COULD GLUE DAD'S BINOCULARS BACK TOGETHER AND HE WOULDN'T EVEN NOTICE! YOU THINK?
IT DEPENDS. WAS THE CASING JUST CHIPPED A LITTLE, OR DID THE LENS ITSELF GET CRACKED?
WELL, MAYBE YOU'D BETTER LOOK AT IT.
DON'T SNEEZE.
WATTERSON

MAYBE YOU SHOULD TELL YOUR MOM ABOUT THE BINOCULARS, AND SHE CAN HELP SOMEHOW.
TELL MOM?!? ARE YOU CRAZY?? NO WAY!
WATTERSON
WHY NOT? YOU'VE GOT TO TELL SOMEONE. MAYBE SHE CAN THINK OF SOMETHING.
AT TIMES LIKE THESE, ALL MOM CAN THINK OF IS HOW LONG SHE WAS IN LABOR WITH ME.

LOOK AT DAD, CALMLY EATING HIS DINNER AS IF NOTHING WAS WRONG.
I KNOW HIM. HIS "DAD RADAR" IS BEEPING LIKE CRAZY. HE KNOWS I BROKE *SOMETHING*, HE JUST DOESN'T KNOW *WHAT*. HE CAN'T NAIL ME UNTIL HE KNOWS FOR SURE. HE'LL JUST WAIT. I KNOW HIM.
HE'S GOING TO JUST SIT THERE EATING AND LET ME STEW IN MY OWN GUILT. HE FIGURES SOONER OR LATER I'LL CRACK.
CALVIN?
AAUGH! I DID IT! I DID IT! I'M SORRY! I DIDN'T MEAN TO!!
..PASS THE UH.. ..THE UH...
WATTERSON

YOU *BROKE* THE BINOCULARS?!
DIDN'T I TELL YOU TO BE EXTRA, EXTRA CAREFUL WITH THEM?? ISN'T THAT EXACTLY WHAT
WELL?!
THOSE BINOCULARS WERE BRAND NEW! HAVE YOU NO RESPECT FOR OTHER PEOPLE'S PROPERTY?!?!
I HAVE AN IDEA, DAD. LET'S PRETEND I ALREADY FEEL TERRIBLE ABOUT IT, AND THAT YOU DON'T NEED TO RUB IT IN ANY MORE.
WATTERSON

I DIDN'T *MEAN* TO BREAK YOUR BINOCULARS, DAD. IT WAS AN ACCIDENT.
(SNIFF) I'M REALLY SORRY. I FELT LIKE I WAS GOING TO BARF ALL AFTERNOON.
WELL, I'M SORRY I YELLED AT YOU LIKE I DID. I SHOULDN'T HAVE BEEN SO ANGRY.
AFTER ALL, IT WAS JUST A PAIR OF BINOCULARS. IN THE BIG SCHEME OF THINGS, THAT'S REALLY NOT SO BAD.
(SNIFF) REALLY?
SURE. ...IN ANOTHER TEN YEARS, YOU'LL PROBABLY BE WRECKING MY *CAR*.
WATTERSON

HOBBES, LOOK! DAD GOT ME MY OWN PAIR OF LITTLE BINOCULARS!
WOW, THESE ARE **YOURS**?
AREN'T THEY GREAT?
I'LL SAY.
DAD SAID AS LONG AS I WAS GOING TO BREAK BINOCULARS, I OUGHT TO AT LEAST BREAK MY OWN.
NOW WE CAN GO TO THE BEACH AND LOOK AT BABES!
MAYBE I SHOULD BREAK DAD'S POWER TOOLS AND SEE IF I COULD GET SOME OF **THOSE**.
WATTERSON

WIND WIND WIND
RUMBLE RUMBLE
POW!
EITHER I'M GREATLY DECEIVED, OR SOMEONE OPENED A CAN OF TUNA IN THIS VICINITY!
YES... ALL OVER THIS VICINITY.
WATTERSON

WHAT A CLEAR NIGHT! LOOK AT ALL THE STARS. MILLIONS OF THEM!
YES, WE'RE JUST TINY SPECS ON A PLANET PARTICLE, HURLING THROUGH THE INFINITE BLACKNESS.
LET'S GO IN AND TURN ON ALL THE LIGHTS.
WATTERSON

Calvin and HobbES
by WATTERSON
I GOT A HIT! I GOT A HIT!
ONLY BECAUSE I LET YOU!
HA HA! A HOME RUN!
YOU DIDN'T TOUCH ALL THE BASES!
I DID, TOO.
NO, YOU DIDN'T. YOU DIDN'T TOUCH SEVENTH BASE.
YES, I DID! I TOUCHED THE WATER BARREL RIGHT AFTER THE FRONT PORCH.
THAT'S NOT SEVENTH BASE. THAT'S TWELFTH BASE!
I THOUGHT THE GARAGE DOOR WAS TWELFTH.
THE GARAGE DOOR IS TWENTY-THIRD BASE. YOU TOUCHED THEM ALL OUT OF ORDER, AND YOU STILL DIDN'T TOUCH THE SECRET BASE.
THE SECRET BASE?? WHAT'S THE SECRET BASE?!
I CAN'T TELL YOU. IT'S A SECRET.
I CAN'T BELIEVE THIS MORONIC SPORT IS OUR NATIONAL PASTIME.
YOU'RE OUT. GIVE ME A DOLLAR.
WATTERSON

Calvin and HOBBES by WATTERSON
zzzzzzzzzzzzzz
FILTH! CONTAMINATION! PESTILENCE! HA HA HA!
OF ALL LIVING CREATURES, FEW ARE MORE REPULSIVE THAN CALVIN THE BUG!
HE EXISTS ONLY TO SUCK BLOOD AND TRANSMIT PARASITIC DISEASE!
SEARCHING FOR SOMEONE TO INFECT, CALVIN FLIES LOW OVER THE PICNIC TABLE!
Ton
INGREDIENTS: SALT.
HIS SENSITIVE ANTENNAE PICK UP THE SCENT OF HUMAN FLESH!
TOUCHING DOWN, CALVIN INSERTS HIS NEEDLELIKE PROBOSCIS INTO A VEIN! PROTOZOANS IN HIS SALIVA QUICKLY INDUCE PLAGUE!
WILL YOU STOP THAT AWFUL SLURPING?! YOU'RE MAKING ME SICK!
WATTERSON

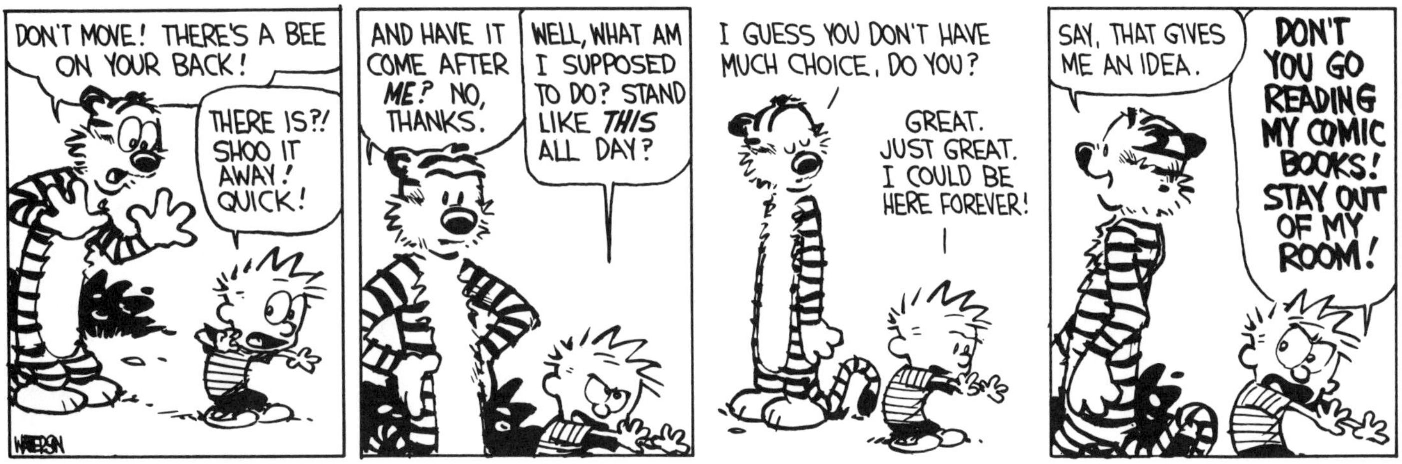
DON'T MOVE! THERE'S A BEE ON YOUR BACK!
THERE IS?! SHOO IT AWAY! QUICK!
AND HAVE IT COME AFTER ME? NO, THANKS.
WELL, WHAT AM I SUPPOSED TO DO? STAND LIKE THIS ALL DAY?
I GUESS YOU DON'T HAVE MUCH CHOICE, DO YOU?
GREAT. JUST GREAT. I COULD BE HERE FOREVER!
SAY, THAT GIVES ME AN IDEA.
DON'T YOU GO READING MY COMIC BOOKS! STAY OUT OF MY ROOM!
WATTERSON

THAT ROTTEN HOBBES! I CAN'T MOVE BECAUSE I'VE GOT A BEE ON MY BACK, SO HE GOES TO READ ALL MY COMIC BOOKS!
HE ALWAYS GETS THEM OUT OF ORDER, AND HE FOLDS THE COVERS BACK! OOH, IF I COULD ONLY MOVE!
WHAT KIND OF FRIEND WOULD TAKE ADVANTAGE OF A PREDICAMENT LIKE THIS? A LOUSY FRIEND, THAT'S WHAT KIND! WHAT A STINKER HE IS!
HEY, DID YOU SEE HOW THE LATEST ISSUE OF CAPTAIN NAPALM ENDED?
DON'T TELL ME! DON'T TELL ME!
WATTERSON

HOBBES, IF YOU TELL ME HOW MY COMIC BOOK ENDS, I'LL KILL YOU. I'VE WAITED ALL MONTH TO FIND OUT.
I'LL GIVE YOU A HINT, OK? CAPTAIN NAPALM TAKES HIS NUCLEAR...
NO HINTS! NO HINTS!
CAPTAIN NAPALM
BY GOLLY, YOU HAIRBALL, IF I DIDN'T HAVE A BEE ON MY BACK RIGHT NOW, I'D...
WATTERSON
MAYBE THERE'S A BEE AND MAYBE THERE ISN'T. I'LL NEVER TELL.
WHAT?! IS THE BEE GONE? CAN I MOVE? TELL ME! IS IT STILL THERE?? HUH? RRGGH! IS IT?!

IS THE BEE STILL ON ME OR NOT?
I'M NOT TELLING. YOU CALLED ME A HAIRBALL.
OK, OK, I'M SORRY. YOU'RE NOT A HAIR-BALL. NOW, IS THE BEE THERE OR NOT?
NO.
GOOD. NOW I...
OWW!!
I MEANT "NO, THERE *IS* A BEE." TODAY IS OPPOSITE DAY!
DON'T FORGET... AT MIDNIGHT OPPOSITE DAY IS OVER, OK?
"YES."

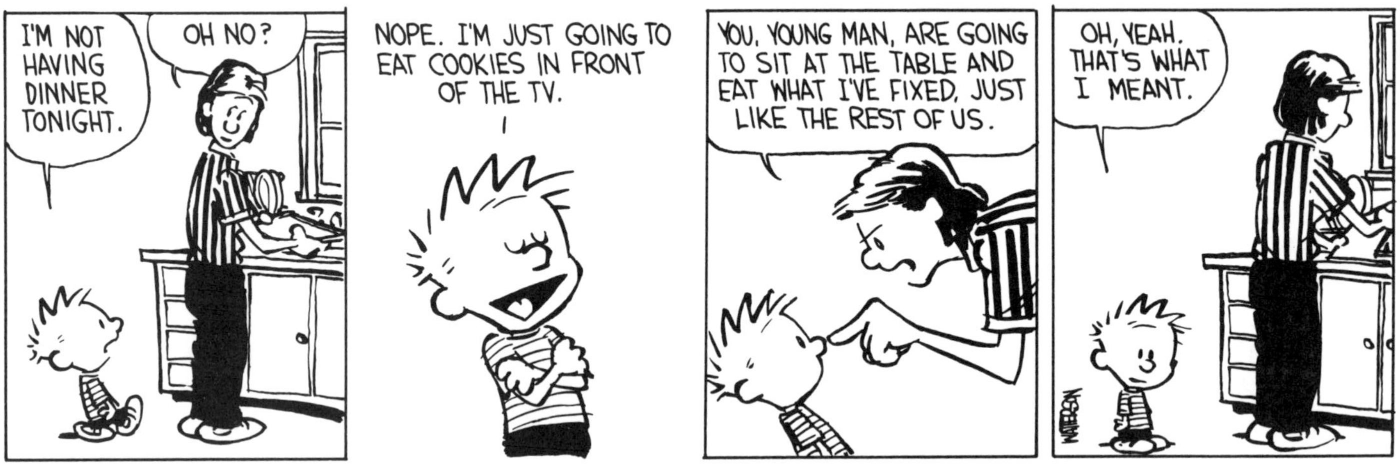
I'M NOT HAVING DINNER TONIGHT.
OH NO?
NOPE. I'M JUST GOING TO EAT COOKIES IN FRONT OF THE TV.
YOU, YOUNG MAN, ARE GOING TO SIT AT THE TABLE AND EAT WHAT I'VE FIXED, JUST LIKE THE REST OF US.
OH, YEAH. THAT'S WHAT I MEANT.

HELLO, I'M WONDERING IF YOU SELL KEGS OF DYNAMITE.
YOU DON'T? HOW ABOUT PLASTIC EXPLOSIVES?
YOU'RE KIDDING. WELL, WHAT ABOUT LAND MINES? DO YOU SELL THOSE? ... YOU DON'T?
LOOK, I'M TRYING TO SEND A GIRL I KNOW INTO DEEP SPACE. PERHAPS YOU COULD SUGGEST SOMETHING.

Calvin and HOBBES
by WATTERSON
FWOOOOSH
AS IF LIFE ISN'T SHORT ENOUGH.
WATTERSON

YOU KNOW WHAT WE NEED, HOBBES? WE NEED AN ATTITUDE.
AN ATTITUDE?
YEAH. YOU CAN'T BE COOL IF YOU DON'T HAVE AN ATTITUDE.
REALLY?
SURE. THEY'RE ALL THE RAGE. NOW WHAT KIND OF ATTITUDE COULD **WE** HAVE?
WE COULD BE COURTEOUSLY DEFERENTIAL.
OH, GOOD. THAT'S **REAL** COOL.

I'VE DECIDED TO BE A FATALIST.
ALL EVENTS ARE PREORDAINED AND UNALTERABLE. WHATEVER WILL BE WILL BE. THAT WAY, IF ANYTHING BAD HAPPENS, IT'S NOT MY FAULT. IT'S FATE.
TRIP
WAUGH!
TOO BAD YOU WERE FATED TO DO THAT.
THAT WASN'T FATE!

DO YOU THINK GROWN-UPS WILL HAVE THE WORLD FIXED UP BY THE TIME THEY HAND IT OVER TO US?
NOT THE WAY THEY'RE GOING.
THAT'S WHAT **I** THOUGHT.
I GUESS THAT MEANS IT'S UP TO **US** THEN.
SOMEHOW, I'M NOT REASSURED.
HA! WHEN **I'M** PRESIDENT, I'LL HAVE THINGS WHIPPED INTO SHAPE IN NO TIME.

EITHER WE'VE GOT TO GET A CATCHER, OR YOU'VE GOT TO IMPROVE YOUR PITCHING.

GOSH, IT SURE LOOKS LIKE RAIN.
RAIN? WHAT ARE YOU TALKING ABOUT? THERE ISN'T A CLOUD IN THE SKY!
YOU DON'T THINK IT LOOKS LIKE RAIN?
NO. GO AWAY AND STOP BEING SILLY.

OK, OUT OF THE HAMMOCK.
WHAT DO YOU MEAN? THIS ISN'T *YOUR* HAMMOCK.
IT'S MY TURN.
I WAS HERE FIRST. IT'S YOUR TURN WHEN I'M DONE.
IF YOU WON'T GET OUT, THEN I'M COMING IN WITH YOU.
LIKE HECK YOU ARE!
THIS CRUMMY HAMMOCK ALWAYS SAGS.

Calvin and HOBBES
by WATTERSON
DO YOU SEE ANY SNAPPING TURTLES, EELS OR LEECHES IN THERE?
NOPE. SO FAR, OUR EXPEDITION IS A FAILURE.
HOW'S THE WATER?
ABSOLUTELY FRIGID. MY FEET ARE COMPLETELY NUMB.
IF I GO IN JUST A HALF-INCH EVERY TEN MINUTES, I CAN STAND IT.
GETTING YOUR SWIMSUIT WET IS THE WORST PART, THOUGH. AS SOON AS IT TOUCHES THE WATER, IT SOAKS UP AND CLINGS TO YOU, AND GETS YOU WET BEFORE YOU'RE READY.
WHY DON'T YOU JUST JUMP IN AND GET IT OVER WITH?
ARE YOU KIDDING? THE SHOCK WOULD KILL ME! IT'S BETTER TO GO IN A WEE BIT AT A TIME.
NO, IT'S BETTER TO DO IT ALL AT ONCE. IT'S WORSE TO DRAG IT OUT.
YOU MUST'VE BEEN DROPPED WHEN YOU WERE LITTLE.
I'LL SHOW YOU! LOOK OUT!
NO! NO! NO!
SPLOOSH!
BRR-R-R-R! MAYBE YOU WERE RIGHT.
WE'LL NEVER KNOW NOW, WILL WE ?!?
WATTERSON

HEY, LOOK! MOM AND DAD ARE THROWING DUFFEL BAGS IN THE CAR. THEY'RE GOING ON VACATION!
AT LAST! FINALLY WE GET THE HOUSE TO OURSELVES! WE CAN STAY UP LATE AND WATCH TV! WE CAN EAT COOKIES FOR DINNER! WE....
WHAT ARE YOU DOING UP HERE STILL? C'MON, LET'S GO.
ME? GO? GO WHERE?
ON VACATION! WHAT HAVE WE BEEN PLANNING ALL MONTH?
WITH YOU AND MOM?? WHAT KIND OF VACATION IS *THAT*?!

SO WHERE ARE WE GOING? I SURE HOPE WE'RE NOT CAMPING AGAIN THIS YEAR.
WELL, WE ARE.
OH, NO! WHY DO WE HAVE TO GO CAMPING?! I *HATE* CAMPING!
SWATTING MOSQUITOES WHILE LYING FROZEN AND CRAMPED ON BUMPY ROCKS, WITH NO TV AND ONLY CANNED FOOD TO EAT, IS *NOT* MY IDEA OF A GOOD TIME!
THAT'S WHY WE BROUGHT BUG SPRAY.
LOOK, JUST LET ME OUT HERE, OK? I'LL HITCH HOME AND SEE YOU WHEN YOU GET BACK, ALL RIGHT?

REMEMBER LAST YEAR, WHEN IT RAINED ALL WEEK? IT POURED SO HARD WE COULDN'T EVEN MAKE A FIRE.
WITHOUT QUESTION, THAT WAS ONE OF THE WORST EXPERIENCES OF MY LIFE.
YES, BUT IT BUILT CHARACTER.
OH SURE.
WHY CAN'T I EVER BUILD CHARACTER AT A MIAMI CONDO OR A CASINO SOMEWHERE?

WELL, HERE WE ARE! HOME AWAY FROM HOME!
OK, CALVIN, YOU GET OUT WITH YOUR MOM, AND I'LL HAND OUR GEAR TO YOU.
NOW DON'T DROP THIS. IT'S VERY...
OOPS.
PLOONK
DON'T WORRY, DAD. IT'S ONLY ABOUT TEN FEET DEEP. I CAN SEE THE CAMERA AND EVERYTHING.
I AM GOING TO FEED YOU TO THE SEA GULLS, KID.
DEAR, YOU CAME HERE TO *RELAX*.

GOSH, THIS WATER'S COLD! HERE, THAT'S ALL I COULD FIND DOWN THERE. GO GET ME A TOWEL, CALVIN.
IT NEVER FAILS. THE ONE BAG THE KID DUMPS IN THE DRINK HAS ALL THE FRAGILE AND PERISHABLE ITEMS IN IT.
WELL, THE WEEK CAN ONLY IMPROVE FROM HERE.
ONE WOULD LIKE TO *THINK* SO.
HEY, DAD, DID YOU MEAN TO STACK THE TACKLE BOX AND ALL THIS ON YOUR GLASSES?

BOY, DON'T GO NEAR DAD. WHAT A GROUCH!
I DON'T SEE WHY HE CAN'T BE CIVIL JUST BECAUSE I ACCIDENTALLY DROPPED A DUFFEL BAG OVERBOARD AND HE BROKE HIS GLASSES.
ARE YOU GOING TO TELL HIM HE LEFT THE CAR LIGHTS ON BACK WHERE WE GOT THE CANOE?
I THINK *YOU* SHOULD TELL HIM.

HEY, MOM, DAD AND I ARE GOING FISHING. DON'T YOU WANT TO COME ALONG?
UGGH, NO. THE LAST THING I WANT TO SEE AT THIS UNGODLY HOUR IS A BUNCH OF SLIMY FISH GASPING AND FLOPPING IN THE SLOP AT THE BOTTOM OF A BOAT.
ALL I'D LIKE TO SEE IS A DECENT NEWSPAPER, A FRESH MUFFIN AND A POT OF REAL COFFEE.
WHY'D WE EVER COME HERE THEN?
GO ASK CONAN THE BARBARIAN.
C'MON, CALVIN. I'LL TEACH YOU TO PUT A WORM ON A HOOK.

AHHH, WHAT A DAY!
UP AT DAWN! FRESH AIR! TRANQUILITY! NO DEMANDS, NO PHONES, NO PRESSURE!
THE WHOLE DAY IS ONE'S OWN! ISN'T THIS GREAT? ISN'T THIS THE LIFE?
SPACEMAN SPIFF, A PRISONER ON THE ZOG SLAVE GALLEY, PLANS HIS DARING OVERBOARD ESCAPE!
AHH, WHAT A DAY!

GOSH, I COULD LOOK AT THE STARS ALL NIGHT.
WITHOUT THE STREETLIGHTS OR POLLUTION HERE, IT SEEMS LIKE YOU CAN SEE FOREVER INTO SPACE.
SNAP
CRUNCH
OF COURSE, IF YOU'VE SEEN ONE STAR, YOU'VE SEEN THEM ALL.
TRUE, TRUE. SHALL WE MOSEY ON BACK TO THE TENT?

LOOK, MOM, THE WATER IS UP TO MY KNEES!
SEE? SEE? LOOK, MOM! THE WATER'S UP TO MY KNEES! SEE? LOOK WHERE THE WATER IS!
NOW LOOK! THE WATER IS HIGHER THAN MY KNEES! SEE? LOOK, MOM! SEE?
I'M ENTHRALLED, CALVIN.
YOU'RE NOT EVEN LOOKING!
WATTERSON

WHATCHA DOIN', DAD? PAINTING A PICTURE?
YEP.
WHAT'S THAT THING? A BRONTOSAURUS WITH RABIES?
IT'S THAT ISLAND OVER THERE.
OH.
WATTERSON
HOW FAR CAN YOU SEE WITHOUT YOUR GLASSES? CAN YOU SEE ME?
WHEN I LOOK UP, I'D BETTER NOT BE ABLE TO.

HI, MOM!
MM.
DAD'S PAINTING A PICTURE, BUT IT'S NOT COMING OUT SO HOT, AND HE'S IN A REALLY STINKY MOOD. IT'S LIKE, I ASKED HIM ONE LITTLE QUESTION AND HE NEARLY BIT MY HEAD OFF! I MEAN, IT'S NOT AS IF I RUINED HIS LOUSY PICTURE, RIGHT? WHY SHOULD...
CALVIN, CAN'T YOU SEE I'M TRYING TO READ?
EVER NOTICE HOW TENSE GROWN-UPS GET WHEN THEY'RE RECREATING?
WATTERSON

THERE'S NOTHING TO **DO** HERE.
THAT'S SORT OF THE POINT, DON'T YOU THINK? IT'S GOOD TO STOP RUNNING AROUND.
SOMETIMES ONE SHOULD JUST LOOK AT THINGS AND THINK ABOUT THINGS, WITHOUT **DOING** THINGS.
YOU'RE CERTAINLY THE EXPERT ON **THAT**.
WHAT I LIKE IS WHEN YOU'RE LOOKING AND THINKING AND LOOKING AND THINKING.... AND SUDDENLY YOU WAKE UP.

MOM, CAN HOBBES COME IN SWIMMING WITH ME?
I DON'T THINK HE'D BETTER, CALVIN.
WHY NOT?
UM... TIGERS DON'T SWIM VERY WELL.
THEY DON'T?
FRANKLY, I'M NOT SURE YOUR MOM KNOWS SO MUCH ABOUT TIGERS.
LOOK, WE JUST WANT TO AVOID AN ARGUMENT, RIGHT?

OK, CALVIN, START PACKING UP. WE'RE GOING HOME.
FINALLY!
NOW, NOW. THESE LITTLE OUTINGS ARE VALUABLE EXPERIENCES.
YEAH? HOW?
THEY GIVE US A CHANCE TO BE TOGETHER AS A FAMILY AND LEARN ABOUT OURSELVES.
LIKE HOW WE CAN'T STAND BEING IN SUCH CLOSE PROXIMITY WITH ONE ANOTHER THIS LONG?
EXACTLY.

Calvin and Hobbes
by WATTERSON
WHAT'S THE SCORE?
TEN BILLION TO ONE, MY FAVOR.
IT IS NOT!
THEN KEEP TRACK YOURSELF.
WHAP!
HA! IT WENT STRAIGHT UP! EASY OUT! EASY OUT!
YOU'RE NOT EVEN GOING TO RUN, EH? I DON'T BLAME YOU. YOU'RE AS GOOD AS OUT.
BINK!
YOU CAN'T DO THAT!
THAT'S TWO HITS ON ONE PITCH! THIS RUN COUNTS DOUBLE!
WATTERSON

Z
LOOK AT YOU. ALL YOU DO IS LIE IN THE SUN.
I HAVE TO.
HOW COME?
TIGERS' TUMMIES ARE SOLAR CELLS.
YEAH, RIGHT.

ARE YOU HOT?
NOT REALLY. WHY?
IT SEEMS WARM TO ME. AREN'T YOU A *LITTLE* HOT?
NOPE.
NOT EVEN A WEE BIT? JUST A SMIDGEN?
WHAT HAVE YOU GOT BEHIND YOUR BACK?

SUSIE, QUICK! GET HELP!
SOMEBODY FILLED MY SANDBOX WITH QUICKSAND! I'M SINKING FAST! ACK! RRGHH!
OH, RIGHT. GIVE ME A BREAK.
YOUR GENDER WOULD BE A LOT MORE TOLERABLE IF IT WASN'T SO DARN CYNICAL!

Calvin and HOBBES
by WATTERSON
SI-I-I-I-IX..... FI-I-I-I-IVE .... FOUR-R-R-R....
THREETWOONE TAG! YOU'RE "IT"!
THAT'S NOT FAIR!
TAG! I GOTCHA!
OK, NOW I'M "IT" AND I HAVE TO CATCH YOU.
BUT WHAT ABOUT A PENALTY? DON'T YOU GO TO "JAIL" AND DO PUSH-UPS FIRST?
WATTERSON
NO, I'M JUST "IT". THERE AREN'T ANY PENALTIES.
NONE?? DON'T I EVEN GET FREE HITS?
FREE HITS?! NO, YOU DON'T GET FREE HITS!
JUST, LIKE, ON THE ARM? I THINK YOU SHOULD HAVE TO GET HIT ON THE ARM.
I DON'T HAVE TO GET HIT AT ALL!
WELL, WHAT ABOUT AN INDIAN BURN THEN? OR NOOGIES? CAN I GIVE YOU NOOGIES?
NO! I'M JUST "IT"! THAT'S ALL THAT HAPPENS!
OK, OK! THAT'S ALL THAT HAPPENS! SHEESH.
IF YOU ASK ME, THOUGH, ANY GAME WITHOUT PUSH-UPS, HITS, BURNS OR NOOGIES IS A SISSY GAME.
WELL, YOU CAN GET HIT IF YOU WANT.

THIS PROBABLY JUST GOES TO SHOW SOMETHING, BUT I SURE DON'T KNOW WHAT.

THERE'S QUITE A BREEZE UP HERE. I'M REALLY MOVING. THERE'S THE RIVER AND THE TOWN TRIANGLE.
HEY, DOWN THERE! MY NAME IS CALVIN! TELL MY TIGER, HOBBES, I'M BLOWING AWAY ON A BALLOON!
CAN ANYONE HEAR ME? TELL HOBBES HE CAN'T READ MY COMIC BOOKS JUST 'CAUSE I'M NOT AROUND, OK?
...OH, YEAH, TELL MY PARENTS WHAT HAPPENED, TOO, ALL RIGHT? HELLO? HELLO?

UH OH, I'M HEADING INTO A FLOCK OF DUCKS!
EXCUSE ME! COMING THROUGH!
PARDON ME! GANGWAY! BEEP BEEP!
...BOY, IF LOOKS COULD KILL.

MY HANDS ARE GETTING TIRED. I'LL TIE THE BALLOON STRING ONTO MY BELT LOOP.
THERE...
WHOOP
SHOOF
IF A PLANE COMES ALONG NOW, I'M GONNA DIE.
WATTERSON

WELL, I SUPPOSE THINGS DON'T GET WORSE THAN HANGING FROM A HELIUM BALLOON A MILE ABOVE SOME UNRECOGNIZED STATE.
OF COURSE, MY GRIP COULD WEAKEN, OR I COULD GET SUCKED INTO A JET INTAKE.
THAT'S ONE OF THE REMARKABLE THINGS ABOUT LIFE. IT'S NEVER SO BAD THAT IT CAN'T GET WORSE.
WATTERSON

BOY, I'M JUST GOING HIGHER AND HIGHER.
I SUPPOSE EVENTUALLY THE PRESSURE IN THE BALLOON WILL BE GREATER THAN THE AIR PRESSURE AROUND IT, AND THE BALLOON WILL...
WATTERSON
POP!

THIS HAS GOT TO BE A DREAM.
WHENEVER YOU FALL FROM TWO MILES UP IN THE SKY, YOU LOOK DOWN, GASP, AND SUDDENLY WAKE UP.
GASP!
GASP
GASP
GASP
GASP
GASP

I WONDER IF MY LIFE WILL FLASH BEFORE MY EYES.
THAT'S THE PROBLEM WITH BEING SIX YEARS OLD...
...MY LIFE WON'T TAKE VERY LONG TO WATCH.
MAYBE I CAN GET A FEW SLOW-MOTION REPLAYS OF THE TIME I SMACKED SUSIE UPSIDE THE HEAD WITH A SLUSHBALL.

SAY, I WONDER IF I HAVE ANY GUM IN MY POCKET. I COULD BLOW A BIG BUBBLE, AND...
NOPE, NO GUM. LET'S TRY THIS POCKET.
MY TRANSMOGRIFIER GUN!!
BOY, THESE THINGS COME IN HANDY ALL THE TIME.

I FORGOT ALL ABOUT MY TRANSMOGRIFIER GUN! NOW I HAVE NOTHING TO WORRY ABOUT!
I'LL JUST POINT IT AT MYSELF AND TRANSMOGRIFY! I'M SAFE!
ZAP

WHERE HAVE YOU BEEN?!? I'VE BEEN CALLING AND CALLING. YOUR DINNER'S COLD, I'M SURE.
I DRIFTED AWAY ON MY BALLOON AND IT POPPED, BUT FORTUNATELY I HAD MY TRANSMOGRIFIER, SO AFTER I MISTAKENLY TURNED MYSELF INTO A SAFE, I TRANSMOGRIFIED INTO A LIGHT PARTICLE AND ZIPPED BACK HOME INSTANTANEOUSLY!
...OF COURSE, IF I'D KNOWN WE WERE HAVING ***THIS***, I WOULDN'T HAVE HURRIED.
SOMETIME YOU SHOULD TRY TRANSMOGRIFYING YOURSELF INTO SOMEONE WHO OCCASIONALLY MAKES AN OUNCE OF SENSE.

CALVIN, I'D LIKE YOU TO PICK UP ALL THE STICKS AND FALLEN BRANCHES IN THE YARD, SO I CAN MOW IT.
WILL YOU PAY ME?
WELL... OK, I'LL PAY YOU A DOLLAR.
A DOLLAR? I WON'T DO IT FOR LESS THAN TWENTY-FIVE!!
IN A MINUTE YOU'LL DO IT FOR NOTHING, JUST BECAUSE I TOLD YOU TO.
...I'LL TAKE THE DOLLAR.
SMART KID.

Calvin and HOBBES
by WATTERSON
SPACEMAN SPIFF EXPLORES THE OUTERMOST REACHES OF THE UNIVERSE.
BY POPULAR REQUEST.
INTREPID EXPLORER SPACEMAN SPIFF LANDS ON AN UNCHARTED PLANET. WHAT STRANGE WONDERS WILL HE DISCOVER HERE?
SPIFF SETS OUT IN SEARCH OF SENTIENT LIFE!
WHAT A STRANGE PLANET THIS IS! ITS SURFACE IS SURPRISINGLY SOFT AND POROUS!
AND HERE CURIOUS GEYSERS BLAST HOT AIR!
!!
SUDDENLY IT DAWNS ON HIM! SPIFF IS NOT ON THE PLANET'S SURFACE AT ALL! HE'S WALKING ON A RECLINING ALIEN!!
OUR HERO SETS HIS DEATH RAY BLASTER.
ZZ.. MMF HM?
WATTERSON

Calvin and Hobbes
by WATTERSON
HERE'S "HAMSTER HUEY AND THE GOOEY KABLOOIE." YOU MIGHT LIKE THIS STORY.
YEAH? HOW GOOD CAN IT BE IF IT HASN'T BEEN MADE INTO AN ANIMATED TV SHOW?
I HOPE TONIGHT'S STORY ISN'T AS BORING AS LAST NIGHT'S WAS. IT PUT ME RIGHT TO SLEEP.
DON'T WORRY. THIS STORY WILL KEEP YOU UP ALL NIGHT.
REALLY? WHAT IS IT?
IT'S CALLED, "THE DISEMBODIED HAND THAT STRANGLED PEOPLE."
GOSH, THIS IS GREAT! HOW CREEPY! I NEVER GET A SCARY STORY! A DISEMBODIED HAND! WOW!
AND YOU KNOW WHAT'S REALLY SCARY? THEY NEVER FOUND IT! TO THIS DAY, NOBODY KNOWS WHERE THE HAND IS!
WATTERSON
IN FACT, THE HAND COULD...
OH NO!! THERE IT IS!
IT'S G-GOT ME!!
GAKK!!
..CALVIN?... ...CALVIN?..
I SHOULD'VE THOUGHT OF THAT YEARS AGO.

LET'S GO, CALVIN! WE'RE ALL READY!
BOY, I HAVEN'T BEEN TO THE ZOO IN AGES.
AND CALVIN'S NEVER BEEN. THIS WILL BE FUN.
I'VE BEEN TELLING HIM ABOUT IT ALL WEEK. HE'S SO EXCITED.
C'MON, CALVIN!
SO WHERE DO WE HAVE TO GO NOW?
BEATS ME. MOM AND DAD ARE ALWAYS DRAGGING US SOME DUMB PLACE.

HOW COME THE ALLIGATORS ARE IN THIS BIG PIT?
SO THEY DON'T GET OUT AND EAT PEOPLE.
DOES THE ZOO EVER THROW ANYONE IN?
DON'T BE SILLY. OF COURSE NOT.
HOW SOON UNTIL WE GO HOME?

LOOK! MONKEYS!
SEE HOW THEY USE THEIR TAILS AND FEET TO CLIMB?
ZOOS LET PEOPLE SEE HOW WILD ANIMALS REALLY BEHAVE.
HEY, LOOK WHAT THAT MONKEY'S DOING! RIGHT IN PUBLIC, TOO! HA HA! THAT'S GROSS! HOW COME I'M NOT ALLOWED TO DO THAT?!
COME LOOK AT THE BIRDS OVER HERE, CALVIN.

WHAT DO YOU THINK OF THE ZOO?
I THINK IT'S KIND OF DEPRESSING.
I ALWAYS FEEL SORRY FOR THE ANIMALS. THEY DON'T HAVE MUCH ROOM TO MOVE, OR ANYTHING TO DO.
THEY JUST SLEEP UNTIL THEY'RE FED.
THAT'S PRETTY MUCH ALL *YOU* DO.
YOU KNOW WHAT I MEAN.

HEY, THOSE KIDS ARE FEEDING THE ANIMALS!
MOM, CAN I GET SOME PEANUTS TO FEED THE ANIMALS?
I'M NOT YOUR MOM.
WHOOP!
ARE YOU LOST? WHAT DOES YOUR MOM LOOK LIKE?
FROM THE KNEES DOWN, SHE LOOKS JUST LIKE YOU.

GOSH, I FOLLOWED THAT LADY HALFWAY AROUND THE ZOO, THINKING SHE WAS MY MOM.
WHY DON'T MOMS WRITE THEIR NAMES ON THEIR CALVES SO THIS KIND OF THING WOULDN'T HAPPEN?
I WONDER WHERE I AM. AND WHERE'S HOBBES? I THOUGHT HE WAS RIGHT WITH ME.
UH OH. WHERE'S CALVIN?
WHY DO THESE LITTLE FAMILY TRIPS ALWAYS TURN OUT THIS WAY? I'M GOING TO SPEND MORE SATURDAYS AT THE OFFICE.

HERE'S HOBBES, BUT WHERE'S CALVIN?
I DON'T SEE HIM.
WHERE COULD HE HAVE GONE? WE JUST TURNED OUR BACKS FOR A MINUTE.
AND WHY DIDN'T HE TAKE HOBBES?
YOU STAY HERE IN CASE HE COMES BACK, AND I'LL GO LOOK FOR HIM.
OK. (SIGH)
BEING A PARENT IS WANTING TO HUG AND STRANGLE YOUR KID AT THE SAME TIME.

SHEESH. CALVIN COULD BE ANYWHERE IN THIS ZOO.
I HOPE HE AT LEAST HAS THE SENSE TO STAY PUT, WHEREVER HE IS.
WHERE WOULD THE LITTLE ROTTER GO IF HE WAS LOST AND SEPARATED FROM HIS STUFFED TOY?
HIS NAME IS HOBBES, AND HE'S... HEY, I'M TALKING TO YOU!!
TIGERS
Panthera tigris

I KNOW! MAYBE CALVIN'S AT THE TIGER PIT, SINCE HE LIKES TIGERS SO MUCH.
HA HA, MAYBE CALVIN'S ***IN*** THE TIGER PIT, SINCE HE LIKES TIGERS SO MUCH.

YOU FOUND HIM! THANK GOODNESS! WHERE WAS HE?
LOOKING AT THE TIGERS.
I FOLLOWED ANOTHER LADY, THINKING IT WAS MOM, AND THEN WHEN I REALIZED I WAS LOST, I WENT TO ASK THE TIGERS IF THEY'D SEEN HOBBES.
NEXT TIME YOU SHOULD ASK A **PERSON** FOR HELP.
...OH... THAT NEVER OCCURRED TO ME.
ONLY NEXT TIME, THERE WON'T **BE** A NEXT TIME, BECAUSE WE'RE JUST GOING TO TIE YOU TO A STAKE IN THE YARD EVERY WEEKEND.
DEAR!
A FAT LOT OF HELP YOUR COMPATRIOTS WERE, I MIGHT ADD.

DO YOU KNOW WHAT DAY IT IS?
NOPE. WHY?
OH, NO REASON. I WAS JUST CURIOUS.
I SURE LIKE SUMMER VACATION.

SO YOU WANT SOME WATER, HUH? WELL, I'VE GOT A BIG CAN OF IT HERE.
IT'S UP TO **ME** TO DECIDE IF YOU GET WATER OR NOT! **I** CONTROL YOUR FATE! YOUR VERY **LIVES** ARE IN MY HANDS!
WITHOUT **ME** YOU'RE AS GOOD AS DEAD! WITHOUT **ME**, YOU DON'T...

Calvin and HOBBES
by WATTERSON
I GOT A HIT!
SAFE!
OK, THAT WAS A SINGLE. I HAVE A GHOST RUNNER HERE NOW, SO I CAN BAT AGAIN.
AND MY GHOST RUNNERS WHO *WERE* ON FIRST AND SECOND BASE ARE NOW ON SECOND AND THIRD, RIGHT?
NOPE. THEY'RE BOTH OUT.
OUT?!
MY GHOST OUTFIELDER TAGGED YOUR GHOST GOING TO THIRD, AND THREW TO MY GHOST SECOND BASEMAN. IT WAS A BRILLIANT DOUBLE PLAY.
THAT NEVER HAPPENED!
YOU'VE GOT TWO OUTS.
WELL, MY GHOST ON FIRST JUST STOLE HOME, SO I'VE GOT ANOTHER RUN! HA HA, SMARTY!
YEAH, WELL, ALL MY OUTFIELD GHOSTS JUST RAN IN AND BEAT THE TOBACCO JUICE OUT OF HIM.
HA! THE GHOST UMPIRE JUST SUSPENDED ALL YOUR GHOSTS FOR ETERNITY. THEY'RE OUT OF THE GAME.
HMPH! IF MY GHOSTS DON'T PLAY, *I* DON'T PLAY.
YOU FORFEIT THE GAME THEN! YOU LOSE AUTOMATICALLY IF YOU QUIT!
THE GHOST CROWD SUPPORTS ME. THEY'RE "BOO"-ING YOU!
SOMETIMES I WISH I LIVED IN A NEIGHBORHOOD WITH MORE KIDS.
WATTERSON

Calvin and Hobbes
by WATTERSON
RUSTLE
RUSTLE
ZING!
WHAM!
WE TIGERS JUST *LIVE* FOR THAT!
NOT FOR LONG, YOU WON'T.
WATTERSON

MOM?
WHAT, CALVIN?
YOU KNOW THE LIVING ROOM COUCH?
WHAT ABOUT IT?
DON'T YOU THINK IT'S TOO WIDE?
I WAS JUST **ASKING**!
WATTERSON

WIND WIND
RUMBLE
OH, NO!
POW!
IT WASN'T TUNA! IT WAS PINEAPPLE! **SEE?!**
ALL CANS SOUND THE SAME.
WATTERSON

THE PROBLEM WITH HAVING A TIGER FOR A FRIEND IS THAT HE ALWAYS APPEARS OUT OF NOWHERE, COMING RIGHT AT YOU AT A GOOD 90 MILES AN HOUR!
AAH!
WHEW I THOUGHT I HEARD HIM. ...GOSH, MY HEART IS STILL POUNDING. WHERE ***IS*** HE ??
OH, ***THERE'S*** HOBBES. THANK GOODNESS.
YOU HAVEN'T BEEN LOOKING WELL, CALVIN. MAYBE YOU SHOULD GO TO BED EARLIER.
WATTERSON

Calvin and Hobbes
by WATTERSON
WOW! HOW DID YOU EVER GET SO MUDDY?!
WELL, I WAS JUST STANDING THERE, MINDING MY OWN BUSINESS, WHEN ALL OF A SUDDEN, A HORDE OF DIRTY CANNIBALS COMES...
FORGET IT.
BOY, WHAT A DELIGHTFUL AFTERNOON.
SOMETIMES I FEEL LIKE I WORK ALL THE TIME TO AFFORD THIS PLACE, AND I NEVER GET TO SIT BACK WITH A GOOD BOOK AND ENJOY IT.
WELL, AT LEAST I HAVE THE WEEKENDS TO...
CALVIN
YOU GOT MUD ALL OVER THE HOUSE! LOOK AT YOU! AIEE - THE COUCH! WHAT'D YOU DO?! DID YOU WALK ACROSS THE COUCH?!
I DIDN'T DO IT! SOMEONE ELSE MUST HAVE! I JUST SAW A MUDDY GUY GO RUNNING FROM...
OUT! OUT OF THE HOUSE! NOW!
OK, OK! I'M GOING! YOU DON'T NEED TO PUSH! I CAN TELL WHEN I'M NOT WANTED! HEY! LEGGO! OW! ALL RIGHT, GOODBYE!
HEY, DAD, CATCH THE WATER BALLOON!
GREAT REFLEXES, DAD. BY THE WAY, DON'T GO IN THE HOUSE LIKE THAT. MOM'S IN ONE OF HER MOODS AGAIN.
I'LL BET I COULD GET A LOT OF WORK DONE AT THE OFFICE ON WEEKENDS...
WATTERSON

BOY, WHAT A BEAUTIFUL SUMMER MORNING, HUH, DAD? TOO BAD YOU CAN'T STAY HOME TO ENJOY IT.
WHEN YOU'RE OLD, YOU'LL BE SORRY YOU NEVER TOOK ADVANTAGE OF DAYS LIKE THESE, BUT OF COURSE, THAT'S FAR OFF, AND IN THE MEANTIME, THERE'S LOTS OF WORK TO BE DONE.
YEP, YOU'D BETTER GO TO WORK. HAVE A GOOD LONG DRIVE IN TRAFFIC. MAYBE YOU'LL GET HOME IN TIME TO WATCH THE SUN SET... IF YOU CAN STAY AWAKE. SO LONG!
GOLLY, I'D HATE TO HAVE A KID LIKE ME.
WATTERSON

WHAT WOULD YOU DO IF I CREAMED YOU WITH THIS WATER BALLOON RIGHT NOW?
TAKE THE WORST THING YOU CAN IMAGINE, AND IMAGINE SOMETHING A HUNDRED TIMES WORSE THAN THAT.
YOU'D DO *THAT*?
NO, I'D DO SOMETHING EVEN WORSE.
WATTERSON
HE PIQUED MY CURIOSITY.

BIP
WHEEEE.
WATTERSON

Calvin and HOBBES
by WATTERSON
THE RACE WILL FINISH AT THAT TREE, OK?
THIS TREE?
RIGHT.
READYSETGO, I WIN!
ON YOUR MARK... ...GET SET....
GO!
HEY! LEGGO!
OW! STOP THAT!
MMF RRG
PUFF PUFF
FINISH! OOF.
TEN MINUTES! THAT'S OUR BEST TIME YET FOR THE 50-YARD DASH!
WATTERSON

WHAT ARE YOU DOING WITH ALL YOUR DAD'S TOOLS IN THE BATHROOM?
THIS FAUCET DRIPS, SO I'M GOING TO FIX IT.
YOU'RE GOING TO FIX IT?
THAT'S WHAT I SAID.
...AND YOU CAN KEEP YOUR COMMENTS TO YOURSELF, DR. DOOM.
I DIDN'T SAY ANYTHING.

FIXING A FAUCET IS EASY. ALL YOU DO IS TAKE IT APART, SEE WHAT'S LEAKING, PLUG IT UP, AND PUT IT BACK TOGETHER.
DOES YOUR MOM KNOW YOU'RE DOING THIS?
NOPE. IT'S GOING TO BE A SURPRISE.
AND WE ALL KNOW HOW SHE LOVES SURPRISES.
I CAN'T GET THIS HANDLE OFF. PASS ME THE HACK-SAW, WILL YOU?

AREN'T YOU SUPPOSED TO TURN THE WATER OFF BEFORE YOU TAKE APART A FAUCET?
THAT'S THE PROBLEM I'M TRYING TO FIX, YOU MORON! I CAN'T TURN THE WATER OFF BECAUSE THE FAUCET LEAKS!
SHEESH, WHERE WERE YOU WHEN THEY WERE PASSING OUT BRAINS?
OH NO! AUGHH! ACKK!
I'LL GET YOU SOME PAPER AND CARBONS FOR YOUR WRITTEN APOLOGY.

HOBBES, QUICK! HOW DO YOU TURN OFF THE WATER ?!?
HOW SHOULD I KNOW ??
I CAN'T PUT THIS PIECE BACK IN WITH ALL THIS WATER COMING OUT!
I'LL GET YOUR MOM!
MY MOM? HAVE YOU LOST YOUR MIND?? SHE CAN'T FIND OUT ABOUT THIS!
I'LL BET SHE NOTICES WHEN THE KITCHEN CEILING STARTS TO DRIP.
OPEN THE MEDICINE CABINET! FIND SOME CYANIDE!

LA DA DEE DEE DA I THINK I'LL GET A BUCKET... DUM DE DOO..
NOTHING'S WRONG...DA DEE DOO BA... I JUST WANT A BUCKET TO HOLD SOME...STUFF. TA TUM TA TUM
LET'S SEE, HOW MANY BUCKETS DO WE HAVE? DUM DE DOO NO CAUSE FOR ALARM... NO NEED TO PANIC ... I JUST WANT A FEW BUCKETS. LA LA.
YOUR TURN.

CALVIN, WHAT ARE YOU DOING?
I'M... UH... GOING TO THE BATHROOM.
FLUSH
IS EVERYTHING ALL RIGHT?
FINE! DON'T COME UP!
FLUSH

WHAT'S ALL THAT WATER I HEAR? I'M COMING IN!
OH MY GOSH! ACKPBT! WHAT'S GOING ON?!? SPLUTB! BPLPTH!
THERE! I GOT THE WATER OFF. ALL RIGHT, CALVIN, WHERE ARE YOU?!
H-HI, DAD.
IT'S THE END OF THE WORLD, CALVIN.

LOOK AT THIS BATHROOM! WHAT ON EARTH WERE YOU DOING?!
NOTHING, DAD! I WAS JUST IN HERE LOOKING FOR SOME DENTAL FLOSS, WHEN PLOOIE! THE FAUCET HANDLE BLOWS SKY HIGH ALL BY ITSELF! IT... IT... UH...
WHAT I MEAN IS, HOBBES WAS FOOLING AROUND WITH YOUR TOOLS. I TRIED TO STOP HIM, BUT HE WOULDN'T LISTEN, AND SURE ENOUGH, HE WENT AND... AND...
ONE MORE TRY.
ALIENS, DAD! BIG, EVIL, BUG-EYED MONSTERS FROM PLUTO! THEY DID IT, AND MADE ME SWEAR NOT TO TELL!

BOY, DAD SURE BLEW HIS STACK THAT TIME, DIDN'T HE? WHAT A SOREHEAD!
LISTENING TO HIM, YOU'D THINK NOBODY IN THE WORLD HAD EVER NEEDED TO CALL A PLUMBER BEFORE. DAD'S GOT A JOB. HE CAN AFFORD IT.
DAD MAKES SUCH A BIG DEAL OUT OF EVERYTHING.
WHEN HE DOES, I SURE WISH YOU'D STOP TRYING TO PIN YOUR CRIMES ON ME.
OH, NOW YOU'RE GOING TO START IN ON ME TOO, HUH?

Calvin and Hobbes
by WATTERSON
DINOSAURS EVERYWHERE FLEE FOR THEIR LIVES!
CALVIN IS COMING!
THE LATE CRETACEOUS: THE LAST EPOCH OF THE MIGHTY DINOSAURS!
KING OF THE THUNDER LIZARDS IS THE FEARSOME CALVIN, THE TYRANNOSAURUS!
SEVEN TONS OF MUSCLE AND TEETH, HE SEARCHES FOR PREY!
CALVIN, FOR GOODNESS' SAKE, STOP STOMPING AROUND! YOU'RE DRIVING ME CRAZY!
OOW!!
CHOMP!
HOW DID THE FEARSOME TYRANNOSAURUS BECOME EXTINCT? NOW WE KNOW!
WATTERSON

WAP
IS THIS YOURS?
NO. WHAT IS IT?
FOR A GIRL, SHE'S REMARKABLY PERCEPTIVE.

GIVE ME SOME COOKIES, OR I LIGHT THE FUSE AND SEND US ALL TO KINGDOM COME!
WHAT DID YOU DO, STICK A PIECE OF STRING INTO A HOT DOG? FOR HEAVEN'S SAKE, DON'T WASTE FOOD, CALVIN. GIVE ME THAT.
CAN I HAVE ANY COOKIES?
NO. GO PLAY OUTSIDE.
I SURE WISH I COULD GET MY HANDS ON SOME **REAL** DYNAMITE.
CAN I HAVE THE HOT DOG, OR DID YOUR MOM TAKE IT?

Calvin and HobbEs
by WATTERSON
I BROUGHT A SCARY STORY OUT, SO WE'RE ALL SET.
WHAT'S IT CALLED?
"THE HIDEOUS MONSTER WHO WAITS IN YOUR BACK YARD TO DISMEMBER YOU."
GOSH, THIS IS THE CREEPIEST STORY I'VE EVER HEARD!
DON'T STOP. KEEP READING.
"SLOWLY THE BOG MONSTER APPROACHED THE INNOCENT CAMPERS. FANGS GLISTENING IN THE MOONLIGHT, IT..."
WHAT WAS THAT NOISE?
OH, STOP IT. THIS IS SCARY ENOUGH.
NO, REALLY, I HEARD SOMETHING! LISTEN!
SNAP!
IT'S THE BOG MONSTER!
OH, NO!! OH, NO!! QUICK, TURN OUT THE FLASHLIGHT! LIE STILL!
WATTERSON
CRUNCH CRACK
IT'S COMING THIS WAY! WE'RE DOOMED!
IT'S GETTING CLOSER AND CLOSER!
ZIPPPPPP!
OH, MY GOSH, IT'S... IT'S OPENING THE TENT FLAP! IT'S COMING IN!
AIEE!
THERE IT IS! BLIND IT WITH THE FLASHLIGHT! PULL DOWN THE TENT POLES! RUN, HOBBES, RUN!
WHAT ARE YOU DOING IN HERE?! WHERE'S YOUR DAD? HE JUST WENT OUT TO CHECK ON YOU.
THE BOG MONSTER MUST'VE GOT HIM!
WHERE'S THAT KID?!

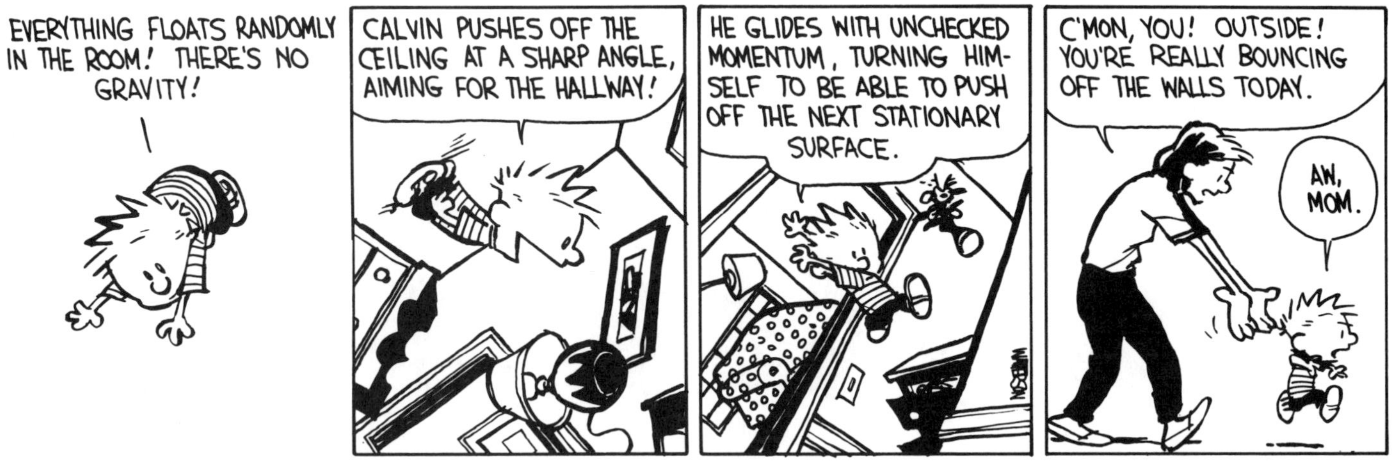
EVERYTHING FLOATS RANDOMLY IN THE ROOM! THERE'S NO GRAVITY!
CALVIN PUSHES OFF THE CEILING AT A SHARP ANGLE, AIMING FOR THE HALLWAY!
HE GLIDES WITH UNCHECKED MOMENTUM, TURNING HIMSELF TO BE ABLE TO PUSH OFF THE NEXT STATIONARY SURFACE.
C'MON, YOU! OUTSIDE! YOU'RE REALLY BOUNCING OFF THE WALLS TODAY.
AW, MOM.

EXTRA PANTS...
THREE SHIRTS, TWO SWEATERS, TWO SWEATSHIRTS...
ANOTHER PAIR OF PANTS...
STILL TRYING TO LEARN TO RIDE THAT BICYCLE, EH?
I DON'T NEED ANY COMMENTS FROM YOU.

A SHADOW FALLS OVER THE LARGE CITY SKYSCRAPERS!
IT'S A GIGANTIC ANT! WITH ONE FOOTSTEP, IT PULVERIZES THE ENTIRE DOWNTOWN! MILLIONS DIE INSTANTLY!
THE ANT BRUSHES THE CITY OFF THE MAP! PEOPLE FLOOD THE STREETS IN PANIC, ONLY TO BE SMASHED IN THE HORRIBLE WRECKAGE!
WELL... MAYBE I WON'T...

WHAT ARE YOU DOING, SUSIE?
DRAWING ON THE SIDEWALK.
WOW! CAN I TOO?
SURE. HERE'S SOME CHALK.
GOSH, I'VE NEVER BEEN A VANDAL BEFORE!
THIS ISN'T VANDALISM. IT WASHES RIGHT OFF!
WATTERSON

OK, I FEEL ONE COMING. ARE YOU READY?
READY.
ACHOOO
POOF
DID YOU GET IT?
YEP! SEE, HERE IT COMES.
BOY, THAT'S A GOOD ONE!
WHY CAN'T MY SCHOOL PORTRAITS EVER LOOK LIKE THIS?
WATTERSON

DON'T COME IN HERE!
WHY NOT? I'M ROASTING.
YOU'LL GET HAIR IN THE WATER. GO DO SOMETHING ELSE.
HEY! STOP THAT! HEY! HEY!
YOU THINK YOU'VE WON, HUH? WELL, I'M NOT EVEN GOING TO TELL YOU WHAT I DID.
ACKPTH!
WATTERSON

Calvin and HOBBES
by WATTERSON
WELL, SUMMER IS ALMOST OVER. IT SURE WENT QUICK, DIDN'T IT?
YEP.
THERE'S NEVER ENOUGH TIME TO DO ALL THE NOTHING YOU WANT.
WATTERSON

TRIP
BAP
WHACK
BAP
WATTERSON

I'M HUNGRY.
TOO BAD. BREAKFAST ISN'T UNTIL TOMORROW.
MY TUMMY'S GROWLING.
HUSH.
MOST PEOPLE DON'T SLEEP WELL NEXT TO A HUNGRY TIGER.
SOMETIMES I SURE WISH I HAD A DOG.
MORE TUNA AND LESS MAYONNAISE.
WATTERSON

OH, NO! THERE'S A TYRANNOSAURUS IN THE GROCERY STORE!
THE DINOSAUR HEADS FOR THE MEAT DEPARTMENT AND DEVOURS THE BUTCHER!
SHOPPERS EVERYWHERE FLEE FOR THEIR LIVES! IT'S MAYHEM, DESTRUCTION AND CARNAGE IN THE AISLES!
WATTERSON
OH, NO! CALVIN, CAN'T I TAKE YOU **ANYWHERE**?!
NOW THE TYRANNOSAURUS WANTS COOKIES!

PLANET CALVIN MOVES ACROSS THE SOLAR SYSTEM.
NOBODY NOTICES UNTIL HIS ORBIT TAKES HIM DIRECTLY BETWEEN THE SUN AND EARTH.
CALVIN CAUSES A TOTAL SOLAR ECLIPSE! EARTH IS SHROUDED IN DARKNESS. HOW LONG WILL CALVIN STAY THERE?!
COULD YOU MOVE, PLEASE? YOU'RE IN MY LIGHT.
HA HA HAAA!
WATTERSON

ELECTION DAY IS COMING UP. HAVE YOU DECIDED ON A RUNNING MATE?
A RUNNING MATE?
SURE. YOU CAN'T BE ELECTED DAD WITHOUT A MOM, RIGHT?
ARE YOU GOING TO KEEP THE MOM I'VE HAD, OR GET A *NEW* RUNNING MATE?
GEE...
BEDTIME, CALVIN.
OF COURSE I'LL STICK WITH YOUR MOM.
AWW..

I THINK RITUALS ARE IMPORTANT.
MY FAVORITE RITUAL IS EATING THREE BOWLS OF "CHOCOLATE FROSTED SUGAR BOMBS" AND WATCHING TV CARTOONS ALL SATURDAY MORNING.
AFTER A FEW HOURS, I'M SO OVERSTIMULATED I CAN'T SIT STILL OR EVEN THINK STRAIGHT.
SORT OF A TRANSCENDENTAL EXPERIENCE, HUH?
YEAH. I ACHIEVE A LOWER CONSCIOUSNESS.
WATTERSON

Calvin and HOBBES
by WATTERSON
CAN I HAVE A DIFFERENT PLATE, MOM?
WHY?
SOMEBODY PUKED ON MINE.
JUST EAT YOUR DINNER AND KEEP QUIET, OK, CALVIN?
EWWWWW
MMF!
HOOPA
GLARGH!
FLIP
FLOP
BLAHHHHHHH
TWITCH TWITCH
OH, KNOCK IT OFF, CALVIN. IT'S HAMBURGER CASSEROLE. THERE'S NOT A THING IN THERE YOU DON'T LIKE.
THIS IS HAMBURGER?
CHEW CHEW
HMM... THIS BITE WASN'T SO BAD, FOR SOME REASON. I WAS ABLE TO CHOKE IT DOWN, ANYWAY. MY STOMACH IS STILL CRAMPING UP, BUT THE PAINS AREN'T AS SHARP ANY MORE. THE SECRET IS TO SUPPRESS THE GAG REFLEX. AFTER I SWALLOW IT, I CAN STAND IT.
GOOD. I'M GLAD THIS IS SUCH A HIT.
WATTERSON

ALL RIGHT, ALL RIGHT! I'M GOING!
HEY! LEGGO! I CAN WALK MYSELF! I JUST HAVE TO... OK! LOOK, I'M GOING! I'M GOING!
SURE, YOU THINK SCHOOL'S GREAT NOW. BUT IN A COUPLE OF HOURS YOU'LL MISS ME! YOU'LL SEE!

THERE GOES CALVIN OFF TO SCHOOL. HE SURE PUT UP A FUSS.
WELL, HE'LL HAVE FUN ONCE HE GETS THERE.
SEE, HE'S EVEN RUNNING NOW. HE'S ALL EXCITED ABOUT...
HEY! CALVIN, THE BUS STOP IS THAT WAY! COME BACK HERE!

I CAN'T BELIEVE I'M HERE WAITING TO GO TO SCHOOL. WHAT HAPPENED TO SUMMER?
GOSH, I COULDN'T WAIT FOR TODAY! SOON WE'LL BE MAKING NEW FRIENDS, LEARNING ALL SORTS OF IMPORTANT THINGS, AND...
WHAT'S THE MATTER WITH YOU ??
YOUR BANGS DO A GOOD JOB OF COVERING UP THE LOBOTOMY STITCHES.

I PLEDGE ALLEGIANCE...
TO QUEEN FRAGG... AND HER MIGHTY STATE OF HYSTERIA...
NCIPAL
IT'S GOING TO BE A LONG YEAR.

Hey, Calvin, you're on my swing. Get lost.
I'M NOT SCARED OF YOU, MOE.
Oh no?
NOPE. YOU'RE SO DUMB YOU PROBABLY NEVER THOUGHT ABOUT HOW A SPARROW'S SMALLER SIZE AND GREATER MANEUVERABILITY IS AN ADVANTAGE IN FIGHTING OFF BIG CROWS.
Yeah?
PUNCH
THOSE TV NATURE PROGRAMS WILL BE THE DEATH OF ME YET.

YES, CALVIN?
MAY I BE EXCUSED, PLEASE?
AGAIN?
I HAVE TO GO. BAD.
ALL RIGHT.
THANK YOU.
WHAT ARE *YOU* DOING HOME?!
I HAD TO GO.

Calvin and HOBBES
by WATTERSON
SCHOOL'S OUT! FREE AT LAST!
AND JUST SIX PRECIOUS HOURS BEFORE BED TO FORGET EVERYTHING I LEARNED TODAY.
I HATE COMING HOME FROM SCHOOL. I NEVER KNOW IF HOBBES IS WAITING TO POUNCE ON ME.
MAYBE I CAN STAND OFF TO THE SIDE HERE, AND PUSH THE DOOR OPEN WITH A STICK.
I'M HOME!
WHAT DO YOU DO, WAIT UNTIL YOU SEE THE WHITES OF MY EYES?!?
BOY, YOU SHOULD'VE SEEN THEM! THEY WERE AS BIG AS DINNER PLATES! HOO HOO HOO!
WATTERSON

HAVE YOU BEEN READING THE PAPERS? GROWN-UPS REALLY HAVE THE WORLD FOULED UP.
ACID RAIN, TOXIC WASTES, HOLES IN THE OZONE, SEWAGE IN THE OCEANS, AND ON AND ON!
THE ONLY BRIGHT SIDE TO ALL THIS IS THAT EVENTUALLY THERE MAY NOT BE A PIECE OF THE PLANET WORTH FIGHTING OVER.

YOU'RE PACKING?
YEP. GET YOUR TOOTHBRUSH, HOBBES. WE'RE OUTTA HERE.
IT'S AN OUTRAGE HOW GROWN-UPS HAVE POLLUTED THE EARTH! I REFUSE TO INHERIT A SPOILED PLANET! I'M LEAVING!
REALLY? WHERE TO??
YOU KNOW, SOMETIMES YOU'RE A REAL LOAD TO HAVE AROUND.
I WAS JUST ASKING!

HOW ABOUT MARS? WE COULD GO THERE TO AVOID EARTH'S POLLUTION.
YEAH! IF WE GO NOW, WE CAN CLAIM IT AND KEEP EVERYONE ELSE OFF IT.
OK, IT'S SETTLED. MARS IT IS.
YOU FINISH PACKING. I'LL GO GET THE WAGON.
WE'RE GOING IN THE WAGON?
OF COURSE! WHAT DID YOU WANT TO DO? FLAP YOUR ARMS?
I GUESS I HADN'T THOUGHT ABOUT THAT PART.
OBVIOUSLY.

SO LONG, MOM. HOBBES AND I ARE GOING TO MARS TO LIVE. EARTH IS TOO POLLUTED.
HAVE A GOOD TIME.
SAY GOODBYE TO DAD FOR US. IF I CAN FIND AN INTERPLANETARY POST OFFICE, I'LL WRITE YOU ONCE IN A WHILE AND...
CALVIN, DON'T STAND THERE WITH THE DOOR OPEN. YOU'RE LETTING IN BUGS. EITHER STAY IN OR GO OUTSIDE.
WATTERSON
SHE DIDN'T SEEM TOO CHOKED UP ABOUT US GOING, DID SHE?
WE SHOULD'VE LEFT A LONG TIME AGO.

BLAST OFF!
DO YOU REALLY THINK WE'LL GET ENOUGH LIFT TO BREAK EARTH'S GRAVITY?
WATTERSON
OF COURSE! YOU THINK I DIDN'T PLAN THIS OUT?! I THOUGHT OF EVERYTHING.
DID YOU THINK OF WHAT YOU'LL EAT ON OUR TRIP?
PACKING WAS YOUR JOB! DIDN'T YOU PACK US ANY FOOD?!?
I PACKED FOOD FOR ME...

WE DID IT! WE CLEARED EARTH'S ORBIT!
WATTERSON
MARS, HERE WE COME!
ARE YOU SURE THIS IS THE WAY?
WHAT? DIDN'T YOU BRING THE MAP?!

SPACE TRAVEL MAKES YOU REALIZE JUST HOW SMALL WE REALLY ARE.
WHEN YOU SEE EARTH AS A TINY BLUE SPECK IN THE INFINITE REACHES OF SPACE, YOU HAVE TO WONDER ABOUT THE MYSTERIES OF CREATION.
SURELY WE'RE ALL PART OF SOME GREAT DESIGN, NO MORE OR LESS IMPORTANT THAN ANYTHING ELSE IN THE UNIVERSE. SURELY EVERYTHING FITS TOGETHER AND HAS A PURPOSE, A REASON FOR BEING. DOESN'T IT MAKE YOU WONDER?
I WONDER WHAT HAPPENS IF YOU THROW UP IN ZERO GRAVITY.
MAYBE YOU SHOULD WONDER WHAT IT'S LIKE TO WALK HOME.

HANG ON! WE'RE COMING IN THROUGH MARS' ATMOSPHERE.
BONK
BONK
WE'VE LANDED! WE'RE THE FIRST ONES TO EVER SET FOOT ON ANOTHER PLANET! WHAT A HISTORIC MOMENT!
I STILL CAN'T BELIEVE YOU FORGOT THE CAMERA.
I REMEMBERED IT. YOU JUST DIDN'T WANT TO TURN AROUND.

SEE ANY SIGNS OF MARTIAN LIFE?
NOT YET...
HEY, LOOK! IT'S THE OLD "VIKING" SPACECRAFT THAT LANDED HERE IN THE '70s!
GOSH, I WONDER IF IT'S STILL WORKING.
BLAHHHH
HOOP HOOP
BOOLA
ACKACKACK
BOOLA
THAT OUGHT TO BLOW SOME CIRCUITS AT NASA!
HEE HEE HEE! I'VE ALWAYS WANTED TO DO SOMETHING LIKE THAT.

WELL, THIS IS OUR NEW HOME. I GUESS WE SHOULD UNPACK AND SET UP CAMP.
COMIC BOOKS... COMIC BOOKS.. TUNA... SOME CANDY BARS... MORE TUNA... TOOTHBRUSHES... A CAN OPENER... LOOKS LIKE WE'RE ALL SET.
WHAT'S THIS?
A NIGHT LIGHT. I THOUGHT IT MIGHT BE SCARY SLEEPING ON A NEW PLANET.
BOY, YOU THOUGHT OF EVERYTHING.
NOW WE HAVE TO FIND AN OUTLET.

YEP, MARS MAY BE A LITTLE DULL, BUT IT'S BETTER THAN EARTH.
CRUNCH CRUNCH
WE'VE GOT A WHOLE PLANET TO OURSELVES. BRAND NEW AND UNSPOILED. NO PEOPLE, NO POLLUTION.
NOTHING BUT RUGGED, NATURAL BEAUTY AS FAR AS THE EYE CAN SEE.
THAT'S NOT YOUR CANDY BAR WRAPPER OVER THERE, IS IT?
IT WAS JUST THERE A MINUTE! *I* WASN'T GOING TO LEAVE IT.

I DON'T KNOW ABOUT YOU, BUT I **LIKE** IT HERE ON MARS.
I DO TOO. IT'S VERY PEACEFUL.
NOT ONLY THAT, BUT WE DON'T HAVE **MOM** HERE TO BOSS US AROUND! NO EARLY BEDTIME, NO BATHS, NO DISGUSTING DINNERS, NO...
DID THAT ROCK JUST MOVE?!?
MOMMMMM!!

OH MY GOSH, THAT ROCK MOVED! THERE'S SOMETHING UNDER IT!
IT MUST BE A MARTIAN! OH NO! OH NO! IT'S PROBABLY SOME CREEPY, TENTACLED, BUG-EYED MONSTER!
YOU'RE RIGHT! THERE'S A TENTACLE NOW!
IT'S COMING OUT! WHAT WILL WE DO?!
AAUGHHHHH
WATTERSON

IS THE MARTIAN STILL OUT THERE?
I'LL TAKE A PEEK.
I DON'T SEE HIM. HE MUST HAVE HIDDEN.
HIDDEN?? DO YOU THINK HE'S SCARED OF US?
WHY NOT? WE'RE SCARED OF HIM.
YEAH, BUT WE'RE JUST ORDINARY EARTHLINGS, NOT WEIRDOS FROM ANOTHER PLANET, LIKE HE IS.
WATTERSON

WHY DO YOU THINK THE MARTIAN HID FROM US?
MAYBE MARTIANS DON'T LIKE EARTHLINGS.
DON'T LIKE US?! WHAT'S NOT TO LIKE?? THERE'S NOTHING WRONG WITH HUMANS!
HEY, YOU MARTIAN! COME ON OUT! WE'RE NOT BAD! WE JUST CAME HERE BECAUSE PEOPLE POLLUTED OUR OWN PLANET SO MUCH THAT... UH.. WHAT I MEAN, IS... UM...
SO WHAT ARE YOU SAYING? THAT OUR REPUTATION PRECEDED US?
WOULD YOU WELCOME IN A DOG THAT WASN'T HOUSE-TRAINED?
WATTERSON

I GUESS WE SHOULD GO HOME TO EARTH.
YEAH, WE MAY NOT BE WELCOME HERE.
WE OUGHT TO FIX UP OUR OWN PLANET BEFORE WE GO MESSING AROUND WITH OTHER PEOPLE'S PLANETS.
AFTER ALL, THERE'S ONLY ONE EARTH, AND IT'S GOT TO LAST US A WHILE.
WE ALSO SHOULD GO HOME BECAUSE WE'RE CLEAN OUT OF TUNA.
I HOPE MOM AND DAD DIDN'T RENT OUT MY ROOM.
WATERSON

THERE'S EARTH! WE'RE ALMOST HOME!
LOOK, YOU CAN SEE THE CONTINENTS.
HMM... IF I REMEMBER MY ATLAS, WE LIVE IN A BIG, PURPLE COUNTRY.
AND OUR HOUSE IS BY THE GIANT LETTER "E" IN THE WORD "STATES."
WATERSON

HI, DAD! GUESS WHAT HOBBES AND I DID! WE WENT TO MARS!
WELL, WELL.
YEP. WE WERE GOING TO LIVE THERE BECAUSE EARTH IS SO POLLUTED, BUT WE DISCOVERED THAT MARS IS INHABITED, SO WE CAME BACK HOME.
YOU DIDN'T LIKE THE MARTIANS?
NO, THEY DIDN'T LIKE US. I THINK THEY WERE AFRAID WE'D JUNK UP MARS THE WAY WE'VE JUNKED UP EARTH.
WHAT'S MY GOOD BRIEFCASE DOING OUT, AND WHY DOES IT SMELL LIKE TUNA FISH?!
AND CAN YOU BELIEVE IT, DAD? WE GO CLEAR TO MARS, AND DUMB OL' HOBBES FORGETS THE CAMERA!
WATERSON

Calvin and HOBBES
by WATTERSON
CALL IT.
TAILS.
OK, BEST TWO OUT OF THREE.
OOOMPH
LET'S CHANGE THIS TO **TOUCH** FOOTBALL, OK?
WATTERSON

FOR SHOW AND TELL, I BROUGHT A SPACE ALIEN I CAPTURED IN MY BACK YARD.
YES, FOR THE LAST TWO DAYS I'VE BEEN KEEPING IT IN THIS SPECIAL ZARNIUM-COATED BAG, AND FEEDING IT PURE AMMONIA!
AND NOW, THE MOMENT YOU'VE ALL BEEN WAITING FOR!
AARGH
HOW'D IT WORK?
MY TEACHER SAYS MOM AND DAD BOTH HAVE TO SIGN MY REPORT CARDS THIS YEAR.

SCOOTCH SCOOTCH
GREETINGS. I AM AN X-387 ROBOT PROBE SENT FROM JUPITER.
MM HMM.
MY SENSORS INDICATE TRACE AMOUNTS OF CHOCOLATE IN THE PANTRY. PLEASE LOAD SOME IN MY SCOOP FOR ANALYSIS.
NO, YOU'LL SPOIL YOUR APPETITE.
MY MISSION MUST NOT FAIL. PREPARE FOR ANNIHILATION, PITIFUL EARTH FEMALE.
GO BACK TO JUPITER, X-3 WHAT-EVER.

YOU KNOW, WHEN YOU THINK ABOUT IT, OUR LIVES ARE PRETTY NICE.
A LOT OF KIDS DON'T HAVE AS GOOD OF A HOME LIFE AS WE DO. WE REALLY CAN'T COMPLAIN.
..WHICH ISN'T TO SAY WE SHOULD GO HOME YET.
WHEN DO YOU THINK THEY'LL SEE THE CAR WINDSHIELD?

Calvin and HOBBES
by WATTERSON
YOU KNOW WHAT WOULD MAKE THIS HOUSE A LOT BETTER?
NO, WHAT?
YOU SHOULD TAKE OUT THE STAIRS AND PUT IN AN ELEVATOR.
GOOD. I'LL FILE THAT WITH YOUR IDEA FOR THE MOVING SIDEWALK.
OH NO!
WHOAAA
OWW
...WWCH!
WHOAAA
OWW
...WWCH!
WHOAAA
OWW
..WWCH!
DID YOU FALL DOWN THE STAIRS AGAIN?!
THAT'S ME (OOF), THE HUMAN SLINKY.

HI SUSIE! GUESS WHAT I BROUGHT FOR LUNCH.
NO! GO SIT BY SOMEONE ELSE, OK? YOU ALWAYS SAY YOUR LUNCH IS SOMETHING REVOLTING, AND I DON'T WANT TO HEAR IT!
GEE WHIZ, WHAT'S WRONG WITH YOU? MY LUNCH IS PEANUT BUTTER. WHAT'S SO DISGUSTING ABOUT THAT?!
HMPH. I'M GLAD THAT ONE DAY OUT OF THE YEAR YOU CAN BE CIVIL.
IT'S MY **DESSERT** THAT'S GROSS! LOOK, A THERMOS FULL OF PHLEGM!

CALVIN, WILL YOU RUN AND GET MY PURSE, PLEASE? I NEED THE CALCULATOR.
SURE.
HERE YOU ARE.
THANKS.
AHEM.
I'M NOT GOING TO TIP YOU!!
HUH! SEE IF I EVER FETCH ANYTHING AGAIN.

ELECTION DAY IS COMING UP, DAD. PEOPLE WANT TO KNOW WHERE YOU STAND ON THE ISSUES.
SUCH AS?
LATER BEDTIMES, EXPANDED TV PRIVILEGES, SHORTER SCHOOL WEEKS, AND LESS DISCIPLINE.
I'M AGAINST THEM ALL.
I SEE.
HOW'S YOUR IRA? PRETTY WELL FUNDED?
GO TO BED.

Calvin and Hobbes
by WATTERSON
UH-OH.
SOMETHING IS VERY WRONG HERE.
CALVIN HAS MYSTERIOUSLY SHRUNK TO A QUARTER OF AN INCH TALL!
HOW CAN HE MAKE HIS PLIGHT KNOWN TO HIS PARENTS WHEN HE'S SMALLER THAN A PENNY?
LIBERTY
1977
CALVIN GETS AN IDEA! HE GRABS THE LEG OF OF A PASSING HOUSEFLY AND FLIES TO HIS DAD'S CAMERA!
ONCE THERE, HE CLIMBS UP AND SETS THE SELF-TIMER.
JUMPING ON THE SHUTTER, CALVIN HAS FIFTEEN SHORT SECONDS TO GET IN FRONT OF THE LENS!
WATTERSON
WITH LUCK, CALVIN'S DAD WILL HAVE THE FILM DEVELOPED SOON, AND DISCOVER WHAT HAS HAPPENED!
WHAT HAPPENED?! LOOK AT ALL THESE TERRIBLE PICTURES! I DON'T REMEMBER TAKING THESE. WHO'S THAT LITTLE SPECK IN THE DISTANCE ALL THE TIME? YOU HAVEN'T BEEN FOOLING WITH MY CAMERA, HAVE YOU?
ME? HECK, NO. MAYBE YOU SHOULD GET THE CAMERA FIXED.

MOMMMM
WHAT'S THE MATTER, CALVIN?
I DON'T FEEL GOOD.
WHAT HURTS?
MY STOMACH. I WANT MOM.
ME? WHAT'S WRONG WITH YOU, FOR CRYING OUT LOUD?!?
YOU CAN ASK HIM. NOW LET ME BACK UNDER THE COVERS.
WATTERSON

SHEESH, IT'S TWO IN THE MORNING. WHY DO KIDS ALWAYS FEEL SICK AT TWO IN THE MORNING?
CALVIN PROBABLY JUST ATE TOO MUCH DESSERT. IF HE'S GOING TO GET ME UP AT THIS HOUR, HE'D BETTER REALLY BE SICK.
BARRRFF
I DIDN'T MEAN IT!
HONEY, PIPE DOWN. I'M TRYING TO SLEEP.
WATTERSON

IT'S BEEN 20 MINUTES SINCE YOU'VE BEEN SICK, SO LET'S TAKE YOUR TEMPERATURE.
IG GOMFA FOME UBHIGGIN.
WHAT'D YOU SAY, HONEY?
IG GOMFA FOME UBHIGGIN.
AACK! WHY DIDN'T YOU SAY SO? GIVE ME THE THERMOMETER! RUN! RUN!
WATTERSON

I THINK THE WORST OF THIS IS OVER, SO JUST TRY TO GET SOME SLEEP.
I'M GOING BACK TO BED, BUT GIVE ME A CALL IF YOU FEEL SICK AGAIN, OK? NOW GET SOME REST.
MM HMM.
POOR LITTLE KID.
YECCHHH! THERE IS NOTHING WORSE THAN A SICK ROOMMATE! FACE THAT WAY!
WATTERSON
IT'S SCARY BEING SICK... ESPECIALLY AT NIGHT.
WHAT IF SOMETHING IS REALLY WRONG WITH ME, AND I HAVE TO GO TO THE HOSPITAL??
WHAT IF THEY STICK ME FULL OF TUBES AND HOSES? WHAT IF THEY HAVE TO OPERATE? WHAT IF THE OPERATION FAILS? WHAT IF THIS IS MY... MY... LAST NIGHT... ALIVE??
THEN I CAN LOOK FORWARD TO HAVING THE BED TO MYSELF TOMORROW.
FEW THINGS ARE LESS COMFORTING THAN A TIGER WHO'S UP TOO LATE.
WATTERSON
FEELING ANY BETTER THIS MORNING, CALVIN?
NO.
I GUESS I'D BETTER MAKE YOU AN APPOINTMENT WITH THE DOCTOR.
OK.
IT'S SATURDAY, BY THE WAY. YOU WON'T MISS SCHOOL.
I KNOW.
WATTERSON

WELL, IT LOOKS LIKE CALVIN JUST CAUGHT THE BUG GOING AROUND. NOTHING SERIOUS.
KEEP AN EYE ON HIM, AND LET ME KNOW IF HE ISN'T FEELING BETTER SOON.
OK. THANK YOU.
SO LONG, CALVIN. YOU WERE A GOOD PATIENT THIS TIME.
MM.
NOTHING LIKE A LITTLE VIRUS TO TAKE THE EDGE OFF A KID.
I'D STILL RATHER LET HIS TEACHER DEAL WITH HIM.

I GET TO STAY HOME FROM SCHOOL TODAY.
I GET TO LIE IN BED, DRINK TEA, AND READ COMIC BOOKS ALL DAY.
I WISH I COULD DO THIS EVERY DAY.
...LIKE SOME PEOPLE I KNOW.
YOUR MOM DOESN'T BRING ME TEA IN BED.

I WANT SOME MORE TOAST.
ROOM SERVICE!!
HA! THAT SURE GOT YOU UP HERE QUICK!
TOMORROW YOU'RE GOING TO SCHOOL.

Calvin and Hobbes by WATTERSON
MY PARENTS ARE THE TWO STUPIDEST PEOPLE ON EARTH.
JUST MY LUCK THEY'D GET MARRIED AND HAVE **ME**.
I HATE EVERYBODY.
I DON'T SEE HOW ANYONE COULD EVER FALL IN LOVE. PEOPLE ARE JERKS.
SOMETIMES THEY ARE, BUT LOOK AT ALL THE COLORS ON THE TREES TODAY.
YEAH? SO WHAT?
I THINK IT'S MORE FUN TO SEE SOMETHING LIKE THIS **WITH** SOMEONE THAN JUST BY YOURSELF.
I **GUESSSS** SO... BUT I'D STILL RATHER SEE THIS WITH A TIGER THAN A PERSON.
WELL, **THAT** GOES WITHOUT SAYING.
WATTERSON

I THINK PEOPLE WORRY TOO MUCH ABOUT LITTLE THINGS.
ALL THEY DO IS MAKE THEMSELVES UNHAPPY THAT WAY.
WHY GET AN ULCER OVER THINGS THAT DON'T REALLY MATTER?
LIKE THE BOOK REPORT YOU'RE SUPPOSED TO BE WRITING NOW ON THE BOOK YOU HAVEN'T READ?
EXACTLY. CASE IN POINT.

WHY IN THE WORLD AM I WAITING IN THE POURING RAIN FOR THE SCHOOL BUS TO TAKE ME SOMEWHERE I DON'T EVEN WANT TO GO?
I GO TO SCHOOL, BUT I NEVER LEARN WHAT I WANT TO KNOW.

I HATE SCHOOL.
EACH DAY I COUNT THE HOURS UNTIL SCHOOL'S OVER. THEN I COUNT THE DAYS UNTIL THE WEEKEND. THEN I COUNT THE WEEKS UNTIL THE MONTH IS OVER, AND THEN THE MONTHS UNTIL SUMMER.
I ALWAYS HAVE TO POSTPONE WHAT I *WANT* TO DO FOR WHAT I *HAVE* TO DO!
WELCOME TO THE WORLD.
WOULD YOU SIGN THIS PARENTAL EXCUSE TO GET ME OUT OF THE NEXT 11½ YEARS OF SCHOOL?

Calvin and Hobbes
by WATTERSON
THE VALIANT SPACEMAN SPIFF, INTERGALACTIC EXPLORER, COMES IN OVER THE MOUNTAINS OF A STRANGE PLANET!
OUR HERO DESPERATELY HOPES TO FIND A REST AREA WITH WORKING FACILITIES.
SPACEMAN SPIFF LANDS ON THE DISTANT PLANET ZOKK!
CLIMBING DOWN FROM HIS SPACECRAFT, OUR HERO PREPARES TO EXPLORE THE SURFACE!
UNEXPECTEDLY, SPIFF'S FIRST STEP SENDS HIM CAREENING THROUGH THE SKY!
SPIFF QUICKLY REALIZES THAT PLANET ZOKK HAS ONLY A FRACTION OF EARTH'S GRAVITY!
OOF
WITH PRACTICE, OUR HERO SOON FINDS HE CAN BOUND EFFORTLESSLY ACROSS THE LANDSCAPE!
WATTERSON
STOP BOUNCING ON THE BED AND GO TO SLEEP!

DUMB BALLOON.
POOF POOF
POOF POOOF
POOFF

HEY, SUSIE, DID YOU HAVE ANY TROUBLE WITH OUR MATH HOMEWORK LAST NIGHT?
NO, WHY?
I THOUGHT A COUPLE OF THESE WERE TRICKY. CAN I CHECK MY ANSWERS WITH YOURS?
OK.
THANKS. WHAT DID YOU GET FOR QUESTION ONE?
SEVEN.
SEVEN? GOOD, THAT'S WHAT **I** GOT. WHAT DID YOU GET FOR QUESTION TWO?
DROP DEAD, CALVIN.

EVER SIT AND WATCH ANTS?
LOOK AT THIS ONE. HE'S CARRYING A CRUMB THAT'S BIGGER THAN HE IS, AND HE'S ***RUNNING***.
AND IF YOU PUT AN OBSTACLE IN FRONT OF HIM, HE'LL SCRAMBLE LIKE CRAZY UNTIL HE GETS ACROSS IT. HE DOESN'T LET ANYTHING STOP HIM.
I JUST CAN'T IDENTIFY WITH THAT KIND OF WORK ETHIC.

Calvin and Hobbes
by WATTERSON
I FEEL A BIG SNEEZE WELLING UP.
...WHICH IS ALWAYS A SURE SIGN THAT I'M NOT CARRYING A HANDKERCHIEF.
AH... AH... AH..
CHOOOOOO!!
MOM, I SNEEZED AND BLEW MY HEAD OFF!
PULL YOUR SHIRT DOWN, CALVIN. YOU'RE NOT FOOLING ANYONE.
MOM WOULD BE A LOT MORE FUN IF SHE WAS A LITTLE MORE GULLIBLE.
WATTERSON

JUST THINK, EARTH WAS A CLOUD OF DUST 4.5 BILLION YEARS AGO...
3 BILLION YEARS AGO, THE FIRST BACTERIA APPEARED. THEN CAME SEA LIFE, DINOSAURS, BIRDS, MAMMALS, AND, FINALLY, A MILLION YEARS AGO, MAN.
NOW IN 1988, THERE'S ME.
... THE ACME OF EVOLUTION.
OH, *PLEASE*.

IT'S NOT QUITE THE SAME, IS IT?
AND IT PROBABLY WON'T SNOW FOR ANOTHER MONTH AT LEAST.

Z
Z
GRRR
Z
GROWLL RRR!
PSST! HEY! WAKE UP! YOU'RE DREAMING!
GRRRR..
AND MOM WONDERS WHY I NEVER LOOK RESTED IN THE MORNING.

Calvin and HOBBES
by WATTERSON
SO THERE YOU ARE! GET OUT RIGHT NOW! INTO THE TUB! LET'S GO!!
SHE'D HAVE NEVER FOUND ME IF I HADN'T SNEEZED.
I'LL GIVE YOU A QUARTER TO TAKE MY BATH FOR ME.
LET'S SEE THE QUARTER FIRST.
HERE. JUST SPLASH AROUND WHILE I MAKE IT SOUND AS IF IT'S ME IN THE TUB.
OK, IT'S A DEAL.
IN FACT, FOR ANOTHER 25 CENTS, I'LL TAKE YOUR WEDNESDAY BATH, TOO.
WOW! REALLY?? I COULD NEVER TAKE A BATH AGAIN!
LA DE DA DA DUM DUM
I'M WASHING MY ARMS NOW! WHOOPS! DROPPED THE SOAP! NOW I'M WASHING MY FACE!
OK, YOU CAN COME OUT NOW. THAT'S LONG ENOUGH.
BOY, THAT WAS EASY. A FEW WEEKS OF THIS AND I'LL BE RICH!
NOT SO LONG WITH THE DRYER. MOM WILL GET SUSPICIOUS.
I'M NOT ALL DRY YET.
ZZZZZ
THERE! WE MADE IT! NOW KEEP A STRAIGHT FACE.
GOOD NIGHT. GIVE ME A KISS.
BLECHH! YOU'RE FILTHY!
DIDN'T YOU HEAR ME TAKE MY BATH?? SEE? MY TOWEL IS WET! SEE? SEE?
I WANT MY QUARTER BACK.
FORGET IT. IT'S AS GOOD AS SPENT.
WATTERSON

LOOK! A BUCKEYE!
ISN'T IT PRETTY? LOOK HOW PERFECT IT IS.
I'M GOING TO KEEP THIS ONE.
WHAT WILL YOU DO WITH IT?
TRY TO DENT SUSIE'S SKULL FROM 50 FEET.
WATTERSON

WHAT ARE YOU DOING?
DAD TOLD ME TO GO OUTSIDE, SO I'M DIGGING A HOLE TO CHINA.
IF DAD'S GOING TO BE SUCH A GROUCH, I FIGURE I'LL JUST GO LIVE ON THE OTHER SIDE OF THE PLANET.
WATTERSON
YOU CAN COME TOO, IF YOU WANT. THERE'S ANOTHER SHOVEL IN THE GARAGE.
YOU DON'T THINK YOUR DAD WILL GET MAD ABOUT US DIGGING UP THE DRIVEWAY?
OH, YOU KNOW DAD. HE'LL GET MAD NO MATTER WHERE WE DIG.

LOOK WHAT MOM MADE ME! A SUPER HERO OUTFIT!
DON'T I LOOK COOL? NOW I CAN FIGHT CRIME WITHOUT ANYONE KNOWING MY TRUE IDENTITY!
YEP, I'M ALL SET NOW!
WATTERSON
...SO! SEEN ANY CRIMES?
WHY DO YOU CARE THAT NOBODY KNOWS YOUR IDENTITY?

CALVIN, TAKE OFF YOUR OUTFIT BEFORE YOU SIT AT THE TABLE, OK?
CALVIN? WHO'S CALVIN? I'M STUPENDOUS MAN!
STOP BEING SILLY, AND DO AS I ASKED YOU.
BUT MOM, I NEED TO WEAR THIS FOR DINNER!
NO YOU DON'T. LET'S GO.
BUT STUPENDOUS MAN HAS A STOMACH OF STEEL!

MOM SAID I CAN'T GO OUTSIDE UNTIL I FINISH MY HOMEWORK. IF YOU'LL HELP ME, I'LL BE DONE FASTER. WHAT'S FIVE PLUS SEVEN?
I DON'T KNOW.
I DON'T EITHER.
THEN WRITE, "I DON'T KNOW."
HEY, THAT'S A TRUE ANSWER, ISN'T IT! I CAN WRITE THAT FOR ALL OF THESE! WE'RE DONE!
WE'D BETTER HAVE A LOOK AT OUR PRODIGY'S HOMEWORK.

WANT TO GO PLAY OUTSIDE?
NO. I'M WATCHING TV.
YOU HATE THIS SHOW. LET'S GO OUT.
NAH.
WHY NOT?
DAD FINALLY SAID HE WAS SICK OF ARGUING WITH ME, AND FOR ALL HE CARED, I COULD WATCH TV UNTIL MY BRAINS OOZED OUT MY EARS.
SO YOU'RE GOING TO?
IT WAS A HARD-WON PRIVILEGE.

Calvin and HOBBES by WATTERSON
FLAPS ....CHECK. FUEL ....CHECK. LANDING GEAR .... CHECK.
GOGGLES... CHECK.
CALVIN PILOTS HIS F-15 AT MORE THAN 1,500 MILES AN HOUR.
LOADED WITH TONS OF EVERY CONCEIVABLE MISSILE, THE JET SHRIEKS LOW OVER THE GROUND!
FWISSHHH!
UP AND OVER THE NEXT RISE, HIS TARGET COMES INTO VIEW! CALVIN FIRES!
MISSILE AFTER MISSILE STREAKS AHEAD AND DETONATES WITH GRIM ACCURACY!
PFOOM!
MISSION ACCOMPLISHED! A SMOLDERING CRATER IS ALL THAT REMAINS OF CALVIN'S ELEMENTARY SCHOOL!
ELEMENTARY SCHO
..SIGH..
WATTERSON

WELL DAD, WE'RE RIGHT DOWN TO THE WIRE, AND THE POLLS SAY YOU WON'T BE DAD HERE MUCH LONGER.
IT SEEMS YOU'RE JUST NOT LIKEABLE ENOUGH. THOSE POLLED CONTINUE TO FIND YOU A COLD FISH.
IF YOU WANT SOME ADVICE, I'D SUGGEST YOU DO SOMETHING EXTRAORDINARILY LIKEABLE IN THE NEXT TWO MINUTES.
GO TO BED.
NO, NO! IT'S WAY TOO LATE TO LEARN HOW TO TELL JOKES.

TEN... FIFTEEN... SIX... TWENTY-TWO...
HIKE!
AUGH!
ANOTHER FIVE YARD LOSS!
WE'VE GOT TO GET SOME OTHER PLAYERS.

BOY, YOU'RE LUCKY YOU DON'T HAVE TO GO TO SCHOOL LIKE I DO.
YOU DON'T KNOW WHAT IT'S LIKE TO GET UP ON THESE COLD, DARK MORNINGS AND HAVE TO GO SOMEPLACE YOU HATE.
YES I DO.
OH YEAH? HOW COULD YOU?
YOU TELL ME EVERY MORNING.
OH, AM I KEEPING YOU AWAKE?! I'M SORRY!

HEY!
THIS (MMF) ISN'T (OOCH) HOW YOU PLAY THE GAME!
YOU STILL HAVEN'T TACKLED ME!

Off the swing, Twinky.
FORGET IT, MOE. I JUST GOT ON. YOU HAVE TO WAIT YOUR TURN LIKE EVERYONE ELSE.
I said, "OFF."
I KEEP FORGETTING THAT RULES ARE ONLY FOR LITTLE NICE PEOPLE.

HIKE!
WHOOPS! HEH HEH..
I'M LOSING THE GAME, BUT WINNING AN AMBULATORY ADULTHOOD.

Calvin and HOBBES
by WATTERSON
RINGGG
WHAT A DAY.
KAPOW
YOU THINK THAT'S FUNNY? COME BACK AND FIGHT, YOU WEASEL!
WHAT HAPPENED TO *YOU*??
DON'T ASK. I'M GOING UPSTAIRS TO CHANGE.
Calvin's ROOM
ENTER & DIE
WATTERSON
NOT AGAAINN!
WHERE'S CALVIN?
I SENT HIM TO HIS ROOM. I CAUGHT HIM MAKING PRANK CALLS TO PET STORES, ASKING IF THEY'D BUY HIS TIGER.

HEY, SUSIE, CAN I BORROW YOUR BLACK CRAYON?
OK, BUT DON'T BREAK IT, AND DON'T PEEL THE PAPER OFF, AND COLOR WITH ALL SIDES OF IT SO IT STAYS POINTY.
GEEZ, WHY DON'T YOU TAKE OUT AN INSURANCE POLICY ON IT?
JUST DON'T RUIN MY CRAYON. WHAT ARE YOU DRAWING ANYWAY?
BLACK BEARS ATTACKING A BLACK FOREST CAMPGROUND AT MIDNIGHT.
GIVE ME MY CRAYON BACK.
WATTERSON

HEY! WHAT'S THIS STUFF IN MY SOUP?!' YECCHH! IS THIS RICE?!? IT HAD BETTER NOT BE!
RICE? LET ME SEE.
LOOK! THESE LITTLE WHITE THINGS! SEE, THERE'S RICE IN MY SOUP! I HATE RICE!
I DIDN'T PUT ANY RICE IN. THOSE ARE MAGGOTS.
EWW, WW!!
ANOTHER LOVELY MEAL AT HOME WITH MY FAMILY. ...I WISH MY JOB REQUIRED MORE TRAVEL.
WELL, HE'S EATING IT NOW, RIGHT?
GOSH, WAIT 'TIL I TELL EVERYONE AT SCHOOL WHAT WE HAD FOR DINNER!
WATTERSON

UH OH.
HOOP
EEP!
I'VE GOT THE HICCUPS SOMETHING TERRIBLE, MOM.
DRINK SOME WATER.
WATTERSON

BANG! I GOTCHA!
ARGG!
GAAACKK
UGHH!
HERE.
WHAT'S THIS?
IT'S YOUR DEATH RATTLE!
SHOOKA SHOOKA
WATTERSON

IT MUST BE AWFUL TO BE A GIRL.
I'M SURE IT'S FRUSTRATING KNOWING THAT MEN ARE BIGGER, STRONGER AND BETTER AT ABSTRACT THOUGHT THAN WOMEN.
REALLY, IF YOU'RE A GIRL, WHAT WOULD MAKE YOU GO ON LIVING?
WATTERSON
THE THOUGHT OF A JERK LIKE YOU BEGGING ONE OF US FOR A DATE WHEN YOU'RE 17.
HA! NOT ME! GROSS!

THE TYRANNOSAURUS STALKS THE CRETACEOUS SHORES!
THE 5-TON CARNIVOROUS LIZARD CAN RUN FASTER THAN A CHARGING RHINO! WHAT COULD BE MORE HORRIFYING?
STOP THAT CLOMPING AROUND!!
...BESIDES THE BLOOD-CURDLING ROAR OF ITS MOM...
WATTERSON

Calvin and Hobbes
by WATTERSON
I'VE NEVER LIKED CRAYONS VERY MUCH.
THEY JUST DON'T HAVE ANY FLAVOR AT ALL.
FOR AN ART PROJECT, I'M SUPPOSED TO DRAW MY PET, BUT SINCE I DON'T HAVE ONE, I'LL DRAW YOU.
OK!
LOOK FEROCIOUS.
HOW'S THIS?
THAT'S GREAT. HOLD STILL, NOW. HMM... ..MM...
ARRGH! THIS ISN'T COMING OUT GOOD AT ALL! I CAN'T DRAW TIGERS! I HATE THIS CLASS!
HERE, LET ME TRY.
THE GOOD THING ABOUT DRAWING A TIGER IS THAT IT AUTOMATICALLY MAKES YOUR PICTURE FINE ART.
HEY, THAT'S PRETTY GOOD!
PUT SOME HUMAN HEADS AROUND HIM, AS IF HE JUST ATE A VILLAGE.
HOW'S THAT?
BOY, THIS IS GREAT! I'LL HAVE THE BEST PICTURE IN THE WHOLE CLASS! I CAN'T WAIT TO SHOW EVERYONE! WOW! THANKS, HOBBES!
BUT I'M NOT LYING! MY TIGER DREW IT! DO YOU THINK I COULD DRAW SOMETHING THAT GOOD MYSELF?!?
YES...
PRINCIPAL

WHEN I GROW UP, I WANT TO BE AN INVENTOR. FIRST I WILL INVENT A TIME MACHINE.
THEN I'LL COME BACK TO YESTERDAY
AND TAKE MYSELF TO TOMORROW
AND SKIP THIS DUMB ASSIGNMENT.

MOMMM, I'M HOME FROM SCHOOL! OPEN THE DOOR FOR ME, OK?
WHAT'S THE MATTER? IT WASN'T LOCKED.
SOMETIMES HOBBES IS WAITING TO POUNCE ON ME AS SOON AS I OPEN THE DOOR.
OH FOR HEAVEN'S SAKE! FROM NOW ON, DON'T CALL ME TO COME TO THE DOOR UNLESS IT'S LOCKED.
HA! I SURE OUT-SMARTED HOBBES THIS TIME!
THBBPTT!
SISSY.

BOY, I'M IN A BAD MOOD TODAY! EVERYONE HAD BETTER STEER CLEAR OF ME!
I HATE EVERYBODY! AS FAR AS I'M CONCERNED, EVERYONE ON THE PLANET CAN JUST DROP DEAD. PEOPLE ARE SCUM.
WELL-L-L? DOESN'T ANYONE WANT TO CHEER ME UP?!?

GET OUT OF MY WAY! I'M IN A BAD MOOD!
?
!
I'LL BET A PET DOG WOULD'VE GOTTEN OUT OF MY WAY.
WATTERSON

WATCH OUT, MOM. I'M IN A BAD MOOD.
BE IN A BAD MOOD SOMEWHERE ELSE, OK? I'M BUSY.
HMPH! I'LL BET MY **BIOLOGICAL** MOTHER WOULD'VE BOUGHT ME A COMIC BOOK AND MADE ME FEEL BETTER INSTEAD OF SHUNNING ME LIKE **YOU**.
KID, ANYONE **BUT** YOUR BIOLOGICAL MOTHER WOULD'VE LEFT YOU TO THE WOLVES LONG AGO.
YEAH, RIGHT. REALLY, HOW MUCH DID YOU PAY FOR ME?
WATTERSON

WHAT'S YOUR TAIL FOR?
MY TAIL?
YEAH. WHY DO TIGERS NEED TAILS?
GEE, I'M NOT REALLY SURE.
I GUESS JUST BECAUSE THEY LOOK GOOD.
WATTERSON
SO IT'S SORT OF A NECKTIE FOR YOUR BUTT?
LET'S NOT BE VULGAR. YOU'RE JUST JEALOUS.

I WISH IT WOULD SNOW EIGHT FEET IN THE NEXT FIVE MINUTES SO THEY'D HAVE TO CLOSE SCHOOL.
C'MON, SNOW! SNOW SNOW SNOW SNOW SNOW SNOW SNOW SNOW!
SO CLOSE... AND YET SO FAR.

DO YOU THINK GOD LETS YOU PLEA BARGAIN?
I'D WORRY MORE ABOUT YOUR MOM.

HELLO?
HI, DAD! IT'S ME, CALVIN. WILL YOU TELL ME A STORY?
CALVIN, I'M AT WORK! I DON'T HAVE TIME TO TELL YOU A STORY NOW! I'M VERY BUSY! GET OFF THE PHONE. I'M EXPECTING IMPORTANT CALLS.
OK, DAD. I'LL JUST STAY HERE QUIETLY GROWING UP AT AN UNBELIEVABLE RATE, NEVER SPENDING MUCH SPECIAL TIME WITH MY OWN DAD, WHO'S ALWAYS WORKING.
RIGHT, RIGHT. THIS IS THE STORY OF THE HYDRAULIC PUMP (Fig. 1), THE WHEEL SHAFT FLANGE (Fig. 2), AND THE EVIL PATENT INFRINGEMENT.
I WANT A GOOD STORY.

Calvin and Hobbes
by WATTERSON
WHO IS THIS MYSTERIOUS MASKED MAN?!?
KAPWIINGG!
AND WHY HAS HE NEVER BEEN PHOTOGRAPHED TOGETHER WITH HANDSOME, 6-YEAR-OLD MILLIONAIRE PLAYBOY CALVIN?
A SOLITARY CAPED FIGURE RUNS ACROSS A MOONLIT BUILDING TOP!
A CRIMSON BOLT BLASTS ACROSS THE NIGHT SKY, STRIKING FEAR INTO THE HEARTS OF ALL EVILDOERS!
YES, IT'S STUPENDOUS MAN, CHAMPION OF LIBERTY, DEFENDER OF FREE WILL!
SOME DIABOLICAL FIEND THREATENS TO ESTABLISH A TOTALITARIAN SYSTEM OF RULE! ONLY STUPENDOUS MAN CAN SAVE THE DAY!
AHA! JUST AS I SUSPECTED! MY EVIL ARCHNEMESIS, MOM-LADY!
DIDN'T I TELL YOU TO GO TO BED?!!?
OH, NO! STUPENDOUS MAN'S STUPENDOUS POWERS ARE NO MATCH AGAINST HIS ADVERSARY! STUPENDOUS MAN IS VANQUISHED!
WATTERSON
THIS WOULD HAVE BEEN PLENTY HUMILIATING WITHOUT THE GOODNIGHT KISS.
AND TAKE OFF THAT SILLY HOOD BEFORE YOU SMOTHER IN YOUR SLEEP.

The End